East Of England
Edited by Claire Tupholme

 Young**Writers**

First published in Great Britain in 2008 by:
Young Writers
Remus House
Coltsfoot Drive
Peterborough
PE2 9JX
Telephone: 01733 890066
Website: www.youngwriters.co.uk

SB ISBN 978-1 84431 602 1

Foreword

Young Writers was established in 1991 and has been passionately devoted to the promotion of reading and writing in children and young adults ever since. The quest continues today. Young Writers remains as committed to the nurturing of poetic and literary talent as ever.

This year's Young Writers competition has proven as vibrant and dynamic as ever and we are delighted to present a showcase of the best poetry from across the UK and in some cases overseas. Each poem has been selected from a wealth of *Little Laureates 2008* entries before ultimately being published in this, our seventeenth primary school poetry series.

Once again, we have been supremely impressed by the overall quality of the entries we have received. The imagination, energy and creativity which has gone into each young writer's entry made choosing the poems a challenging and often difficult but ultimately hugely rewarding task - the general high standard of the work submitted ensured this opportunity to bring their poetry to a larger appreciative audience.

We sincerely hope you are pleased with this final collection and that you will enjoy *Little Laureates 2008 East Of England* for many years to come.

Contents

Jessica Pavitt (9)   1

Bacton Community Primary School, Stowmarket
Daniel Tomlin (9)   2
Jack Rampley (9)   3
Liam Hutchinson (8)   4
Frankie Pinner (9)   5
Emma Martin (8)   6
Verity Ward (9)   7
Joshua Barnes (9)   8
Bethany Stanton (8)   9
Lois Balfour (9)   10
Imogen Mulley-Forsdike (8)   11
Harry Jolly (9)   12
Owen Last (8)   13
Dorothy Tidman (8)   14
Chloe Studd (8)   15
Kirsty Scarff (8)   16
Kira Steggall (8)   17
Lauren Lowings (9)   18
Guy Ward (9)   19
Chloe Warnes (9)   20
Fenella Laflin (8)   21
Abigail Feavearyear (9)   22
Abbie Holden (9)   23
Joe Madgwick (9)   24
Caleb Mellen (8)   25

Beehive Preparatory School, Ilford
Radha Patel (8)   26
Maryam Khaliq (8)   27
Shamayn Hussain (9)   28
Reiss Patel (8)   29
Neel Patel (8)   30
Sakeena Liaquat (9)   31
Sarah Ugradar (9)   32
Faheem Aziz (8)   33
Bissma Ahmed (9)   34
Arun Bacheta (9)   35

Kiran Thavapatham (9)   36
Shuaib Mirza (8)   37
Zahra Nisa Ahmed (9)   38
Reece Holman (8)   39

Commonswood JMI School, Welwyn Garden City

Connor Dodds (11)   40
Jonathan Brind (11) & Lewis Barnes (10)   41
Harry Claridge & Alex Smith (9)   42
Alex McIntyre & Paige Gibbons (8)   43
Andrew Bambury (9)   44
Ben Clark (9)   45
Tomas Martins (10)   46
Elisabeth Spencer-Stallard (9)   47
Jack Burgess (10)   48
James Dolan (11)   49
Charlotte Wesson (9)   50
Emma Perley (11)   51
Cherry-Mae Whitehead (10)   52
Siân Zwager (11)   53
Lauren Allerton (7)   54
Harrison Elliott (10)   55
Lewis Barnes (10)   56
AJ Joseph Turnbull (11)   57
Alex Williams (11)   58
Michaela Davis (10)   59
Carrie Fisher (11)   60
Hannah Curtis (11)   61
Jade Winch (10)   62
Sophie Voutt (9)   63
Amy Smith (10)   64
Bailey Kennoy (7)   65
Tyler Buckingham (8)   66

Edward Worlledge Middle School, Great Yarmouth

Kimberley-Ann Hume (11)   67
Mariah Murray (11)   68
Stefanie Dominguez (11)   69
Ricardo Carvalho (11)   70
Emily Rose Weymouth (8)   71
Louise Taylor (8)   72

Pagan Stamp (8)	73
Cengiz Gilgil (9)	74
Fawn Doggett (9)	75
Kai David Jones (8)	76
Cameron Brackley (9)	77
Sashka Borgenvik (8)	78
Lewis Howard (9)	79
Courtney Emblem (9)	80
Ben Dowell (9)	81
Sophie Brown (8)	82
Sophie Speight (9)	83
Courtney Farrow (11)	84
Kirsty Goodwin (11)	85

Gidea Park College, Romford

Nathan Kurien (9)	86
Briana Longe (10)	87
Samuel Chapman (10)	88
Jessica Hawkes (10)	89
Saif Imran (10)	90
Jack Keys (10)	91
Ankita Gupta (10)	92
Rachael Rawlins (9)	93
Niharika Thakur (9)	94
Jonathan Willans (10)	95
Priya Bhargava (10)	96
Finley Miles (10)	97
Afreen Hossain (10)	98
Sophie Perry (10)	99
Jonathan Singh (9)	100
Emily Pettitt (10)	101
Chloe Stephenson (9)	102
Fiyinfoluwa Olayide (10)	103
Tuhina Amin (9)	104

Goodrington School Ltd, Hornchurch

Caroline Enaw (8)	105
Katherine Leggat (8)	106
Terry Blackham (10)	107
Amy McLean-Nelson (9)	108
Caitlin Alice Terry (10)	109

Jack Harper (10)   110
Funmi Adeotoye (9)   111
Acacia London (9)   112
Harrison McCann (9)   113
Daria Koukoleva (9)   114
Jasmine Langan (9)   115
Katie Hastie (9)   116
Xavier Farnham-Pegley (8)   117
Amy Storrar (9)   118
Fadere Sorunke (8)   119

Hainford Primary Partnership, Norwich
Alexandra Le Mesurier (9)   120
Katie Grimmer (9)   121
Grace Mellows (9)   122
Sydnie Snowling-Dunford (9)   123
Daniel Porter (8)   124

Marian Vian Primary School, Beckenham
Jessie Rose Ross (10)   125

St Helen's Primary School, Ipswich
Victoria Addison (11)   126
Francesca Mulvey (10)   127
Oscar Anderson (11)   128
Elana Muncey (11)   129
Flora Calivangue (7)   130
Esther Noble (8)   131
Kean Fry (9)   132
Rhiannon Lugo (8)   133
Max Bird (7)   134
Rebecca Rouse (8)   135
Musomie Aktar (7)   136
Stefan Osman-Wiggan (11)   137
Ella Rayment (9)   138
Molly Gooding (7)   139
Toni-Ann Martin (9)   140
Kingsley Corrall (11)   141
Josemar João (11)   142
Alice Todd (10)   143
D'andre Satchwith-Clarke (11)   144

Andrew Bolt (10)   145
Amoke Bowman-Boyles (9)   146
Jake Teague (11)   147
Shahnaz Rahman (11)   148
Tansie Shoults (10)   149
Charlie Fitch (11)   150
Charlie Andrews (11)   151
Natasha Smith (7)   152
Tiffany Evripidou (11)   153
Chloe Stygall (10)   154
Anna Mulvey (8)   155
Amy Goodger (8)   156

St Michael's Woolmer Green Primary School, Knebworth
Emily Grace Wintle (11)   157
Mollie McCormack (9)   158
Daniel Hill (10)   159
Chloé Allanson (10)   160
Daniel Porter (10)   161
Megan Bone (9)   162
Savannah Lamars (9)   163
Philip Taylor (11)   164
Matthew Haumann (9)   165
Kieran Mason (11)   166
Lewis Robins (10)   167

St Paul's CE JMI Primary School, Kings Langley
Lauren Payne (10)   168
Libby Radford (10)   169
Georgia Ware (11)   170
Joshua White (10)   171
Robert Braban (10)   172
Chloe Coxill (10)   173
Molly Gurr (11)   174
Emily Hardway (11)   175
Joely Harris (11)   176
Lillian Holmes (11)   177
Curtis Lake (10)   178

St Pierre School, Leigh-on-Sea

Harrison Wheeler (8)	179
Lily Ella Bovill (8)	180
Andrew Snell (8)	181
Ella Kingsbury (8)	182
Joshua Bull (7)	183
Rupert Abel (9)	184

Springfield Junior School, Ipswich

Chloe Quinton (9)	185
Caitlin Chatfield (9)	186
Gemma Addison (8)	187
Kyle Ferguson (9)	188
Kathy Burch (9)	189
Holly Brown (9)	190
Calvin Footer (9)	191
Téa Addison (8)	192
Luke Addison (8)	193
William Seager (9)	194
Jessica Harrison (8)	195
Ivan Trewern (9)	196
Bethany Brown (8)	197
Kai Coe (8)	198

Westwood Primary School, Hadleigh

Jessica Lacey (8)	199
Rosie Pountney (8)	200

The Poems

Flash

The creeping floors
And opening of doors
Windows banging, lights flashing
The whistle of the wind
Ghosts swishing and swaying side to side
Tables lifting up
Chairs are breaking up
The plates and saucers are smashed against the wall
Ghosts are whispering while sliding down the hall.
Chairs are rattling up high
A flash of lightning
A ghost appears and says, 'Boo'
Glass is smashed, then he flashed
I am the ghost named Flash
I flash here, I flash there
I flash high, low and down below
Scaring people every day tend to make them go away
Blood dripping down the wall tends to make people fall
Rattling of teeth makes you chatter even though it doesn't matter.

Jessica Pavitt (9)

And That's Sooo Not A Lie

Vegetables are my favourite food
And that's sooo not a lie.
Chocolate is a revolting food
And that's sooo not a lie.
I have £50 million
And that's sooo not a lie.
I wrestled aliens on Mars
And that's sooo not a lie.
I fought for the Romans
And that's sooo not a lie.
I was born in the Stone Age and brought up by apes
And that's sooo not a lie.
I'm related to God
And that's sooo not a lie.
Next week I'm going in my private jet to my private island
And that's sooo not a lie.
You don't believe me do you? It's obvious I'm such a liar
And that's sooo not a lie.

Daniel Tomlin (9)
Bacton Community Primary School, Stowmarket

That's Not A Lie

I'm 99 years old
And that's not a lie.
I can jump off a motorbike
And that's not a lie.
I can swim 3,000 metres across the sea
And that's not a lie.
I can drive a lorry without a driving licence
And that's not a lie.
I am the star of the school
And that's not a lie.

Jack Rampley (9)
Bacton Community Primary School, Stowmarket

That's Not A Lie

I can get drunk in one second
And that's not a lie
I can build
And that's not a lie
I am 99 years old
And that's not a lie
I can jump off a motorbike
And that's not a lie
I can drive a car without a driving licence
And that's not a lie
I can do every football skill in the world
And that's not a lie
I can be horrid
And that's not a lie
I can be the best footballer in the world
And that's not a lie
I can drink all of the beers in the world
And that's not a lie
I can play for Chelsea
And that's not a lie
I have seen all of the Chelsea players
And that's not a lie, sorry that I have been telling fibs.

Liam Hutchinson (8)
Bacton Community Primary School, Stowmarket

That's Not A Lie

I can get drunk in 1 second,
And that's not a lie.
I'm 10 years old
And that's not a lie.
I can do anything I like,
And that's not a lie.
I can run faster than a lion,
And that's not a lie.
I can swim 6 metres,
And that's not a lie.
I can read a book in 4 minutes,
And that's not a lie.
I don't have to go to school
And that's not a lie.

Sorry I've been telling lies.

Frankie Pinner (9)
Bacton Community Primary School, Stowmarket

That's Not A Lie

I can get drunk in 1 second
And that's not a lie.
I am 10 years old
And that's not a lie.
I don't have to go to school
And that's not a lie.
I can trash the school
And that's not a lie.
I can be a superhero
And that's not a lie.
I can have a baby
And that's not a lie.

Emma Martin (8)
Bacton Community Primary School, Stowmarket

I Pinky Swear It's True

I can eat three million crocodiles,
I pinky swear it's true.
I can build three whole cities with my left hand only in three
                                                        seconds flat,
I pinky swear it's true.
I can get drunk in two seconds with Coca-Cola,
I pinky swear it's true.
I have travelled round the world when I was 1 year old,
I pinky swear it's true.
My hair is thirty metres long,
I pinky swear it's true.
I can stop and start time,
I pinky swear it's true.
I met everyone famous when I was 2 years old,
I pinky swear it's true.
I can drink 4,000 whole glasses of water without going to the loo,
I pinky swear it's true.
I can make my teacher not give me homework,
I pinky swear it's true.

I know, I know, I am a liar,
But not a bigger liar than *you!*

Verity Ward (9)
Bacton Community Primary School, Stowmarket

Sadness

Sadness is like raiding rabbits
It tastes like muddy mushrooms
It smells like sour apples
It looks like a stopped clock
It sounds like a mad baby
It feels like ragged rocks.

Joshua Barnes (9)
Bacton Community Primary School, Stowmarket

Scared

Scared is like witches everywhere.
It tastes like nightmares everywhere.
It smells like a rotten cup of tea.
It looks like a family with no home.
It sounds like anger everywhere.
It feels like a ghost in your brain.

Bethany Stanton (8)
Bacton Community Primary School, Stowmarket

Sadness

Sadness is like raindrops falling from the sky.
It tastes like teardrops falling from your eyes
It smells like apple pie.
It looks like a shivering fly.
It sounds like screams passing by.
It feels like a falling star.

Lois Balfour (9)
Bacton Community Primary School, Stowmarket

And That's Not A Lie

I can eat 5 pieces of pizza and chips in one second
And that's not a lie.

I have met all the High School Musical stars
And that's not a lie.

I can write 20,000 words in 2 seconds
And that's not a lie.

I own 50 quad bikes
And that's not a lie.

I own 500 dogs
And that's not a lie.

Everybody knows me
And that's not a lie.

Everybody in the school thinks I'm fabulous
And that's not a lie.

I have a private jet
And that's not a lie.

I am the biggest diva in the school
And that's not a lie.

Imogen Mulley-Forsdike (8)
Bacton Community Primary School, Stowmarket

And That's Not A Lie

I can drive my dad's monster truck any time I want
And that's not a lie.
I can buy everything in the world in 1 second
And that's not a lie.
I've got a lion in my bag
And that's not a lie.
I'm the ruler of the world
And that's not a lie.
I'm in the 2008 Formula One race
And that's not a lie.
I can drive a Ferrari
And that's not a lie.
I've seen Cristiano Ronaldo
And that's not a lie.
I'm a big liar
And that's not a lie.

Harry Jolly (9)
Bacton Community Primary School, Stowmarket

Excitement

Excitement is like a fresh apple from the finest tree.
It tastes like a lovely piece of chocolate cake baked fresh today.
It smells like a bar of soap from an expensive smelly set.
It looks like ice cream sundae ready to eat.
It sounds like someone calling you from the sky so beautifully.
It feels like a soft cushion from an angel.

Owen Last (8)
Bacton Community Primary School, Stowmarket

And That's So The Truth

I can climb up the Eiffel Tower and down again in no seconds
And that's the truth.
Zac Efron is my brother
And that's the truth.
I'm the queen of the world
And that's the truth.
I'm magical so you better watch out
And that's the truth.
I will never die when you shoot me
And that's the truth.
People think I'm their god
And that's the truth
And there's the truth *not.*

Dorothy Tidman (8)
Bacton Community Primary School, Stowmarket

And That's Not A Lie

I'm a famous singer
and that's not a lie.
I can fly anywhere in 1 second
and that's not a lie.
I'm an adult
and that's not a lie.
I'm the queen of the whole world
and that's not a lie.
I'm a millionaire
and that's not a lie.
I will never die
and that's not a lie.
I have 1 million houses
and that's not a lie.
I'm a princess
and that's not a lie.
Every person knows me in the whole world
and that's not a lie.
I promise you I love to lie.
I promise you this is not a lie.

Chloe Studd (8)
Bacton Community Primary School, Stowmarket

And That's So Not A Lie

I can swim in 1 minute
And that's so not a lie.
I can eat 1,000 apples
And that's so not a lie.
I am the best swimmer
And that's so not a lie.
I go to knitting club
And that's not a lie.
I am 99 years old
And that's so not a lie.
I am the biggest liar.

Kirsty Scarff (8)
Bacton Community Primary School, Stowmarket

And That's The Total Truth

I have got a private jet
And that's the total truth
I am David Beckham's sister
And that's the total truth
I live in Las Vegas
And that's the total truth
I don't go to school
And that's the total truth
I've been on Big Brother
And that's the total truth

All this is the truth and nothing but the truth.

Kira Steggall (8)
Bacton Community Primary School, Stowmarket

It's No Lie

I'm a famous superstar
and that's no lie.
I have control over the whole world
and that's no lie.
I'm the best robber in the world
and that's no lie.
I'm the Queen's daughter
and that's no lie.
I'm the Underpant King's daughter
and that's no lie.
I have gigantic ears
and that's no lie.
I have the biggest rose in the world
and that's no lie.
I'm the biggest fibber in the world
So it's not a lie!

Lauren Lowings (9)
Bacton Community Primary School, Stowmarket

Anger

Anger is like a fireball through your soul.
It tastes like a chilli explosion in your mouth.
It smells like a burnt piece of toast.
It looks like someone's red face.
It sounds like an angry crowd of people.

Guy Ward (9)
Bacton Community Primary School, Stowmarket

Sadness

Sadness is like raindrops coming off a roof.
It tastes like lemonade with no fizz.
It smells like thin, fresh air.
It looks like raindrops pattering on a window.
It sounds like nobody is around.
It feels like the whole world is gone and nobody cares.

Chloe Warnes (9)
Bacton Community Primary School, Stowmarket

And That's The Total Truth

I can be rich and beautiful in one second
And that's the total truth.
I live in Hollywood
And that's the total truth.
I am a queen of silly
And that's the total truth.
I do not have to do any homework
And that's the total truth.
I am a ruler of the world
And that's the total truth.
I am a rock star
And that's the total truth.
I can eat a restaurant in 3 seconds
And that's the total truth
And all of that was the total truth.

Fenella Laflin (8)
Bacton Community Primary School, Stowmarket

And That's Sooo Not A Lie!

I'm the Queen of England
and that's sooo not a lie.
I can sneeze 100 times in 1 second
and that's sooo not a lie.
I can go to school whenever I want
and that's sooo not a lie.
My body is made of gold and silver
and that's sooo not a lie.
I'm the richest girl in the universe
and that's soo not a lie.
I live on the sun
and that's sooo not a lie.
My mums getting married on the moon
and that's not a lie.
My family are aliens from Mars and Pluto
and that's soo not a lie.
I can rebuild the world in 1 second
and that's soo not a lie.
So now do you believe that you need to be my friend.

Abigail Feavearyear (9)
Bacton Community Primary School, Stowmarket

And That's Sooo The Truth!

I've got all animals in my pocket
and that's soo the truth.
I could make the world pink
and that's soo the truth.
My name is Posh
and that's soo the truth.
I'm the most popular girl in school
and that's soo the truth.
I've got £9,999 in my bank account
and that's soo the truth.
My body is as hard as steel
and that's soo the truth.
I have a private limo
and that's soo the truth.
I'm a famous singer
and that's soo the truth.
I've got a bodyguard
and that's soo the truth.
I've got a hot boyfriend
and that's soo the truth.
I've got 10,000 friends
and that's soo the truth.
I live in a mansion
and that's soo the truth.
I have a posh private school
and that's soo the truth.
I am a time lord
and that's soo the truth.
I can go home during school
and that's soo the truth.
OK, alright
I'm the biggest liar in school
and that's soo the truth.

Abbie Holden (9)
Bacton Community Primary School, Stowmarket

Scared

Scared is like a picture with no harmony.
It tastes like salt and pepper.
It smells like complete nothingness.
It looks like a black and empty room.
It sounds like screeching.
It feels like being alone.

Joe Madgwick (9)
Bacton Community Primary School, Stowmarket

Lies

I can run round the world in one second
and that's not a lie.
I can run faster than a bullet
and that's not a lie.
I can climb Everest in a mini second
and that's not a lie.
I can kill a dinosaur with my bare hands
and that's not a lie.
I have ten extra arms on my back
and that's not a lie.
I can make time go as quick as light
and that's not a lie.
I can double every number in the world
and that's not a lie.
I can fun faster than a cheetah
And that's not a lie.
I can perform miracles everywhere
and that's not a lie.
I have got all the books in the world
and that's not a lie.
I am the strongest person on Earth
and that's not a lie.
I'm the liar and that's not a lie!

Caleb Mellen (8)
Bacton Community Primary School, Stowmarket

Wishes

I wish I was a fairy
floating in the sky.
I wish I was a queen
wearing expensive clothes.
I wish I had fairies' power
so I can soar through the sparkling sky.
I wish I can swim
with dolphins that have golden necklaces.
But the thing I wish for the most is my sister,
I wish she wouldn't chat a lot.

Radha Patel (8)
Beehive Preparatory School, Ilford

My Daughter

She lives in a castle.
She's my daughter.
She wears a crown.
She has a beautiful dress.
She looks lovely. .
She loves to smile.
She gets to do what she wants.
I like my jewellery.
I like my friends.
I am so beautiful.
You will faint when you see how beautiful I am.
I have make-up.
My make-up is as beautiful as me.
You will never guess who I am.

Maryam Khaliq (8)
Beehive Preparatory School, Ilford

Mummy's Massive Bag

On my mum's 21st birthday
My auntie brought her this massive bag
And when my mum told me
One day to get her notebook
From that massive bag
I went in
And what a surprise
Inside it there was a sock
A gorilla which looked like a rat
A 60 foot snake
And last of all, dynamite
I tried getting it out
But bad luck
I still didn't get the notebook.

Shamayn Hussain (9)
Beehive Preparatory School, Ilford

My Flying Car

My flying car is a fast car,
It can take you very far.
It sways to the left,
It sways to the right,
It takes me up to the moon
And brings me back at noon.
It disappears in the sky,
And reappears nearby.
Once again it races a plane
But fails again
But beats a train
And that's my flying car.

Reiss Patel (8)
Beehive Preparatory School, Ilford

Aboard

I visited a ship in Pakistan
It was bright with gold painting, saying *'We hate children'*.
But I found my way to the ship's bow,
I climbed a few steps,
Which were as high as a 30 centimetre ruler.
I could not believe my eyes,
Pirates were fighting viciously.
I was caught and was brought to fight the captain.
I swung the sword,
Cut off one of his hands.

A minute had gone,
The captain's hand came to life.
I ran but I saw another boat
Coming towards the boat I was on.
I wanted to go home,
There was a way out,
To jump into the sea,
The other boat was getting closer.
Crash!
I jumped in the sea
The ship followed me.
Now I was back in the boat again.

Neel Patel (8)
Beehive Preparatory School, Ilford

My Carpet

My carpet is a flying carpet
It goes wherever I want it to go
It is the best thing in the world.

I can take me to see
Princesses, knights, pirates, cowboys, fairies, queens, anything!

Last time I went
I saw an Indian princess
And she needed help.

And when it was 6.00
I told my carpet to go
All the way back home!

Sakeena Liaquat (9)
Beehive Preparatory School, Ilford

If I Were Prime Minster

If I were Prime Minister
Fun would be everywhere
Children have lots of sweets
And adults wouldn't dare
No more school, homework or tests
Pools and fountains would be everywhere
Cinemas, bowling and water parks
Fun and gum and lots of stars
So many things I can't think of them all
Please come and help me through
When holiday makers come for a day
We have bodyguards to make sure
It is a million a day
I have enjoyed it with you
Telling what I'd do
I hope you have enjoyed it
And if you were Prime Minister what will you do?

Sarah Ugradar (9)
Beehive Preparatory School, Ilford

Dragons

It flies around breathing fire everywhere
It burns down cottages, trees and even buildings
It takes away people and takes them to his cave
And he gobbles them up
It is a nasty creature crawling around everywhere
Stomping his feet everywhere
It has lots of friends so you'd better watch out!
Even if it dies its friends come and kill the person who killed it
It can never be defeated
It just carries on burning down cottages
It always keeps coming and coming.

Faheem Aziz (8)
Beehive Preparatory School, Ilford

Adventures To Come True

In the parcel,
There was a present.
In the present was a box
And in that box was
Nothing, nothing and nothing.

But at night fairies came
And sprinkled spells
Into the box.

In the morning
A girl in that house
Wished to be on a flying carpet
And have dreams
And her wish came true.

Bissma Ahmed (9)
Beehive Preparatory School, Ilford

In The Dead Dark

It sounds like wind striking my body,
A very cold one,
It tastes like the cold air
In the Atlantic
It smells like being in snow lands
With your nose dead
It looks like a black devilish monster
Coming towards me
It feels like I am going to collapse
Into a million pieces
It stings like nettles
In my back
It stings like my bones
Will break
I am so scared
It's like an ice box
Has gone down my back
It reminds me
Of the graveyard at night.

Arun Bacheta (9)
Beehive Preparatory School, Ilford

My Smelly Brother

My brother, he's really smelly,
But a bit funny.
He goes around making sounds
Like a big ape in a zoo when I look at him.
He really is dark and light,
But if he was chocolate
He would be mixed and taste yuck.
Sometimes people laugh at him
Because he smells like an old sock.
He is weird.
When I look at him
He makes me smile.
When I hug him,
He feels like a beanbag.
But he reminds me of Henry VIII.
Even though he's my smelly brother
That doesn't change anything.
He's still my brother.

Kiran Thavapatham (9)
Beehive Preparatory School, Ilford

My Flying Carpet

My flying carpet
Flying high and high
In the blue or dark skies.

I will see sights
So wonderful and new
I will see rivers and seas blue.

My flying carpet
Flying high and high
Up and up it goes in the sky.

Shuaib Mirza (8)
Beehive Preparatory School, Ilford

My Magic Box

I have a magic box,
With all my dreams and hopes in.
A magic box I have
With my adventures in.
So magic box
Where shall we go today?
Take me oh magic box
To a smiley hot place.
Do dreams come true there?
Now let us go.
Adventures, princess, cowboy, Queen Victoria.
Take me anywhere,
Oh my magic box,
Where shall we go today?

Zahra Nisa Ahmed (9)
Beehive Preparatory School, Ilford

Inside My Magic Box

(inspired by 'Magic Box' by Kit Wright)

In my magic box
There is a pile of crocs
And a group of dogs with lots of spots
But there's more

There is a group of dragons
Getting ready for their pageants
But there's still more

There is a magic pear
And a grizzly bear
There's still more

There's some magic beans
And the lion gives them a great big beam
And there's a whole lot more.

Reece Holman (8)
Beehive Preparatory School, Ilford

Dleszoli

D riving through the sky like a bird.
L iving in a world long before time.
E agles zoom past me as I go the wrong way,
S o you might have guessed I'm flying my own way.
Z e French are below, I'm going so fast.
O ld people have heart attacks as I'm zooming past.
L ying, sitting, dying and much, much more.
I felt all this while I ate my Weetabix.

Connor Dodds (11)
Commonswood JMI School, Welwyn Garden City

Snowflake

S wiftly, silently, falling on a mission to blanket the land.
N o one will be upset, they will be filled with joy.
O n Christmas Day is the targeted date.
W hen they wake it will be a white, happy Christmas.
F ields slowly begin transformation as the snow settles.
L akes frozen, dead.
A s Christmas Day arrives, the mission is finally complete.
K ids race downstairs with happiness, it has snowed on
                                                    Christmas Day!
E veryone is thrilled with the great day.

Jonathan Brind (11) & Lewis Barnes (10)
Commonswood JMI School, Welwyn Garden City

Fire Snake

I spot a fire snake.
Its jaws are snapping,
The fire is crackling,
Trapped behind the fire grate.

The fire is hissing.
Snake slips and slides,
As the flames whip and glide.
The coal is fizzing.

Snake eyes glowing.
Scales red and bright.
Ready to jump and fright,
Body sweeping and swaying.

Harry Claridge & Alex Smith (9)
Commonswood JMI School, Welwyn Garden City

The Mysterious Burning Fire

Sizzling like the blazing hot sun,
It will burn the crust off a hot cross bun.
Glowing like the dragon's eye,
Same temperature as an overcooked pie.
Black puffs of smoke rising from the fire,
The smoke is jet-black, as black as a tyre.
Spitting like the python's fang,
The fire hears it and makes a monstrous bang!

Alex McIntyre & Paige Gibbons (8)
Commonswood JMI School, Welwyn Garden City

Winter Woods

As the winter evening settled,
A blanket of snow,
White as a polar bear's chest.
The bare trees swayed,
In the breeze.
Footsteps trampled the snow,
And crackled the frosted leaves below.
The blanket settled,
And the sun poked through,
The purest clouds,
Pearly snow drooped from,
The lifeless trees,
And joined the blanket snow.
Around the winter moons,
Were frozen rings of,
Glistening ice.

Andrew Bambury (9)
Commonswood JMI School, Welwyn Garden City

The Senses At Wembley Stadium

Such a sight I saw,
The wonderful Wembley Stadium, it's so big.
Its shining bright lights on the swooping arch.
It made me feel excited.
Such a sight I saw.

And such a sound I heard,
The huge crowd cheering for their team.
I wanted to join in with the screaming and shouting.
It was so loud.
Such a sound I heard.

Such a smell I smelt,
The smell of the delicious burgers with ketchup.
It was tasty and made me feel more hungry.
I felt the air coming on from where they were getting sold.
Such a smell I smelt.

Such a feeling I felt,
The round white ball flew into the air, I punched it.
It went to a player and he caught it without trying.
It felt like I was in the game.
Such a feeling I felt.

Such food I tasted,
The food was the best I've tasted.
It went so quickly the burger and crisps.
I felt I couldn't eat any more.
Such good food I tasted.

Ben Clark (9)
Commonswood JMI School, Welwyn Garden City

Burning Fire

Fire, burning like a volcano.
Moving like a slithering snake.
Twisting and turning, destroying the forest.
The fire so hot, burning people's skin.
Flames swiftly swayed in the cold, frosty air.
Quickly dissolving and increasing.
Wind blows against the fire, causing it to grow.

Tomas Martins (10)
Commonswood JMI School, Welwyn Garden City

The Battlefield

Glistening water surrounds the tree,
Now alone, it stands on its island,
Its branch an armed warrior,
A dagger in its long bony fingers.
The sky like a gentle wave rolling by,
The glittering frost like a murderer,
Sucking the very life from the tree,
Feeding on the living nature.
The frost whispers its secret message,
The tree's hand creaks in the breeze,
Its last and only reply.

Elisabeth Spencer-Stallard (9)
Commonswood JMI School, Welwyn Garden City

Snow

Dancing gracefully through the air,
Drifting slowly to the frosty floor.
Graceful beauty, with the world it wants to share.
Fingers stretching from mountains to shore.
Coats glistening like the stars.
A heart of pure whiteness.
Blankets of snow cover the ground,
Softly touching the ground where it lies.
Gently covering the floor without a sound.
Deep enough to reach your thighs.

Jack Burgess (10)
Commonswood JMI School, Welwyn Garden City

The Blitz

Fear spreads through the town, like butter on toast.
People run to the Anderson Shelter, fearing for their lives.
You try to go to sleep, but the bombs are as loud as a tiger's roar.
Wardens roam for hurt and dying, like a mother searches for cubs.
Relief when the sirens go off. But not now - they're still buzzing on.
Planes drop containers of death, raining down on all.
Kids wonder if their parents are still out there.
Bombs falling from planes way up in the sky.
Tears of death and pain flood the city.
All is dark and will remain that way.
It is over but not for long. Pray to God you still have your life.
Tears stream out as you know all is lost.
The Anderson shelter's ordeal is now over.

James Dolan (11)
Commonswood JMI School, Welwyn Garden City

The Colours Of Life

I'm powerful,
With all my wonderful colours.
Red, green, pink and blue.
I get all the colours.
I get all the world.
The grass is green and the sky is blue.
I make a better world.
My world is bright and shiny,
A wonderful world made by me.
I was the one who made the colours of the world.

Charlotte Wesson (9)
Commonswood JMI School, Welwyn Garden City

War

Bullets firing like bees zooming through the air.
Smoke like an angel letting out a slow breath.
Buildings falling down like dominoes collapsing.
The light was like a firework exploding.
Anderson shelters, like a mother protecting her young.
Air raid siren-like people shrieking.
Aeroplanes like a tornado, taking everything away.
Fear spreads the city like melting butter on toast.
Buildings destroyed like walking over a volcano that has erupted.
Germans laugh as they drop their bombs from above.

Emma Perley (11)
Commonswood JMI School, Welwyn Garden City

The Dream-Making Sea

As I sleep,
The dreams come,
Of water and adventure and love.
The killer whale glides silently through the ocean.
I can hear the lapping of the water, the swirling of the sea,
It lulls me in to an even deeper sleep.
As I dream, the seals dive making small ripples,
Not knowing what awaits them in the watery depths.

I watch the glistening water reflect the ghostly clouds,
That hides the moon and its light in my mind.
My heart aches as I imagine the baby seal alone, helpless, frightened!
The love I have for all sea creatures' whales, seals and otherwise,
Wouldn't be any use to any other race.
I wake suddenly and look out of my window.
The whale is indeed there, but all the seals are safely on the shore.
Instead the killer whale dives for a shoal of fish.
Then turning its huge, elegant body it silently disappears to the watery
home it knows.
I go back to sleep, to my dreams of water, adventure and love.

Cherry-Mae Whitehead (10)
Commonswood JMI School, Welwyn Garden City

Snow Covered

Sitting by the dancing flames.
Outside the snow raging.
Too fast to count the snowflakes.
The door nudges open to reveal a snow-covered man.
Shivering, shaking, never ever breaking.
A cold breeze flies in from the east.
By morning the frost man will be gone.

Siân Zwager (11)
Commonswood JMI School, Welwyn Garden City

My Winter Box

(Inspired by 'Magic Box' by Kit Wright)

I will put in my box . . .
The swish of an angel's wing,
A gentle snowflake shimmering near a star,
A penguin in a cold winter storm.

I will put in my box . . .
A shining moon near the glittering star,
The decorative tassel on a chocolate blanket,
A sweet for a Christmas party in Santa's grotto.

Lauren Allerton (7)
Commonswood JMI School, Welwyn Garden City

War Poem

A shield slashing through the sea's giant claws,
Like a chainsaw through a leaf.
Hands protecting the innocent within,
Soldiers standing like scared rabbits.
Pythons spitting venom at the innocent.
Throbbing engine, a drumbeat of death.

Taking their last breath of life.
Water and blood filling lungs.
Icy water takes their souls.
Water turning red like a weeping ruby.
The monster swallowing its victim.
Destruction of souls, once brave men.

Hiding behind hedges, waiting to charge,
Though a maze of death and destruction.
Ceaseless gunning by the Germans.
Lost souls and trails of death.
Roars of guns, explosions of bombs.
A stench of death fills the air.

Harrison Elliott (10)
Commonswood JMI School, Welwyn Garden City

The Beaches Of Normandy

Certain doom starts approaching.
The sound of sergeants, barking out the orders.
The disgusting stench of sick in the boat.
Soldiers petrified as they jump into the salty sea.
The killer bullets hit the metal, while searching for their victim,
Making a clanging noise.
The nervous, heart-breaking sound of soldiers' shouts and screams.
The waves crash up the beach, adding fear and effort into the fight.
The smell of sick and smoke creep up their noses.

Lewis Barnes (10)
Commonswood JMI School, Welwyn Garden City

Keeper Of Secrets

I am the keeper of all secrets.
Keeper of the memories that you most fear.
East is the way to find you dear.
Young and old, the secrets I keep them all.
Secrets and memories, over them I rule.
Hitting his sister while others took the blame, who knew?
Eating all the biscuits, ripping all the stitches to name but a few.
Resting minds let him collect his treasure.
After the treasures are stolen they are kept forever.
Taunting and teasing you with the key.
My name is Keysherant, keeper of all secrets.
I have everything you know.
Nothing now, your mind is as pure as snow.

AJ Joseph Turnbull (11)
Commonswood JMI School, Welwyn Garden City

The War Poem

Prayers made for hope of survival.
Hearts beat like the throbbing on an engine.
Bullets rampage and rip against metal.
Monstrous waves grasp the boat,
Sea claws men down for all eternity.
Blood stains the sea ruby red.

Gear sinks to the bottom of the sea.
Bullets burn holes in hearts.
The relentless sea claims its victims.
Men drawn deep beneath the waters.
So few make it to land,
Dodging the rain of bullets from above.

Bullets wail across the beach.
Men protected by the hedges.
A maze of danger and explosions.
Not a game of twists and turns, but of death.
Treacherous bullets are fired.
A heartbreaking encounter of death.

Alex Williams (11)
Commonswood JMI School, Welwyn Garden City

How The Snow Lives

Snow drifts from side to side,
A lost passenger on a deserted island.
Snowflakes reach out and join together,
Twisting and turning wanting it to last forever.
Resting its blanket onto the earth,
Falling asleep in the pale moonlight,
Silently and deftly moving through the night.
Covers the country and town,
The sun appears washing it away,
Gone, to return another snowy day.

Michaela Davis (10)
Commonswood JMI School, Welwyn Garden City

The Weather

A giant blanket of snow covers the city,
Gentle wind whispers through the trees,
A face of pure snow covering the ground,
The body of ice lies still and frozen,
The cold raindrops begin to fall,
Tears of love from the heavens above,
The cold rain melts the heart of ice.

Carrie Fisher (11)
Commonswood JMI School, Welwyn Garden City

Snow

Snowflakes fall from the misty sky,
Dancing in the wind as they drop.
Gently they lay sleeping through the night.
A white blanket covers unseen fields.
The wind controls their movement,
Never wishing to turn back.
Just floating in the winter breeze.
Their icy cold fingers touch your heart,
Then slowly fade away at dawn.

Hannah Curtis (11)
Commonswood JMI School, Welwyn Garden City

Ngbubon

I am the water in the tap,
The sand on the beach.
I am the maths that teachers teach.
I am the light in the sun,
The shine in the stars.
I am the darkness in the night
And the speed in racing cars.

I am the hands on the clock,
The whiteness of your teeth.
I am the soil beneath your feet.

Jade Winch (10)
Commonswood JMI School, Welwyn Garden City

The Creator

I am the creator of sound, the maker of music,
Tapping the golden piano, playing the silver flute.
I am also the creator of light, the maker of the sun,
I make everything colourful and fun.
I am the Earth's core, burning fire every day,
I am Hell making everyone miserable, making everyone pay.
Puswoboom, Puswoboom,
You are trapped, left in my way.
Puswoboom, I am the creator of everything forever, for evermore.
He is back and he is coming.
Behold his name.
Puswoboom.

Sophie Voutt (9)
Commonswood JMI School, Welwyn Garden City

Grandad

I had a big grandad that laughed and smiled.
I had a big grandad that was worth the while.
I had a big grandad that was the best.
He seriously was not a pest.

I have a big grandad and I love him so.
I'll never get tired of telling him no.
So, I'm here today to say goodbye,
And good luck with your life so high in the sky.

Sweet dreams Grandad.

Amy Smith (10)
Commonswood JMI School, Welwyn Garden City

The Winter Box

(Based on 'Magic Box' by Kit Wright)

I will put in my box . . .
The warm smell of sage and onion stuffing,
A soft cuddly toy snowman,
A teddy bear cracker with silver ribbons keeping it together.

I will put in my box . . .
A shiny picture of a house in Peterborough,
Brightly decorated with colourful,
Red, yellow and green glowing lights.

I will put in my box . . .
A model of Mary and Joseph,
A little baby sleeping in a bed of hay,
Three kings with three presents.

I will put in my box . . .
A cosy woollen hat,
Melted snow spray,
A white paper snowflake.

I will put in my box . . .
The frosty night air,
The excited faces of children,
Looking forward to their presents.

Bailey Kennoy (7)
Commonswood JMI School, Welwyn Garden City

Monster Flames

The flames are rushing in and out,
Steaming like a hot kettle spout.
Pouring like an angry bear,
Red and orange everywhere.
Spreading as fast as a racing car at top speed.
It's glowing like a goldmine and popping like popcorn seed.
It's as loud as an erupting volcano.
It smells like burnt toast.
Its flames are rising and rising,
Until it reaches the smoky night sky.
The black ashes fall like feathers out of the monster flames.

Tyler Buckingham (8)
Commonswood JMI School, Welwyn Garden City

Frosty And White

It's misty and dark
No sunshine about
Maybe we will have snow
But I doubt.

The sunshine has died
The sun has gone for a run
But now it's winter
It's starting to be fun.

It might rain
It even might snow
At wintertime we remember the man
Who goes ho, ho, ho!

When it rains
The snow will go
And that will be the end
Of Mr Ho, Ho, Ho!

Kimberley-Ann Hume (11)
Edward Worlledge Middle School, Great Yarmouth

The Little Teddy Bear

My teddy sounds like a cat purring.
My teddy smells like strawberry and chocolate.
My teddy tastes like ice cream melting on your tongue.
My teddy looks like a princess.
My teddy feels like fluffy kittens.
My teddy reminds me of my family.
My teddy feels like a pillow.

Mariah Murray (11)
Edward Worlledge Middle School, Great Yarmouth

Sweets Talk

It sounds like a mouse squeaking in your ears.
It smells like chocolate grease.
It tastes like strawberry yoghurt.
It looks like the luxurious candyfloss.
It feels like spongy bubblegum.
It reminds me of my first sweet.

Stefanie Dominguez (11)
Edward Worlledge Middle School, Great Yarmouth

Justice Is Justice

Justice is justice
Its punishment and reward
It's the smell of victory
It sounds like cheering
It tastes like three victories put together
Also it looks like the blue sky.

Ricardo Carvalho (11)
Edward Worlledge Middle School, Great Yarmouth

Love

Love is pink like candyfloss.
It tastes like candy.
It looks like a rose.
It sounds like hearts beating.
It feels like gentleness.
 . . . Love.

Emily Rose Weymouth (8)
Edward Worlledge Middle School, Great Yarmouth

Love

Love is red like roses up a tree.
It tastes like squishy marshmallows and a cup of tea.
It smells like fresh air in the sky.
It looks red and black.
It sounds like singing birds.
It feels like love
   . . . Love.

Louise Taylor (8)
Edward Worlledge Middle School, Great Yarmouth

Love

Love is red like a woolly jumper.
It tastes like warm roses.
It smells like warm chocolate.
It looks like red roses.
It sounds like a bird singing.
It feels like a warm jumper.
Love.

Pagan Stamp (8)
Edward Worlledge Middle School, Great Yarmouth

Anger

Anger is black like an angry bull.
Anger tastes like rotten eggs.
It smells like burnt toast.
It looks like a big, mad bull.
It sounds like a roaring tiger.
It feels like a volcanic eruption.

Cengiz Gilgil (9)
Edward Worlledge Middle School, Great Yarmouth

Heartbreak

Heartbreak is black like a deep hole.
It tastes like burnt toast.
It smells like rotten eggs.
It looks like a dark winter's night.
It sounds like a howling dog.
It feels like being alone.
. . . Heartbreak.

Fawn Doggett (9)
Edward Worlledge Middle School, Great Yarmouth

Tiredness

Tiredness is red like heat.
It tastes like hot chocolate.
It smells like a new teddy.
It looks nice and cosy.
It sounds like a sleeping teddy.
It feels like a warm bed.
   . . . Tiredness.

Kai David Jones (8)
Edward Worlledge Middle School, Great Yarmouth

Fear

Fear is black like the darkest cave.
It tastes like a monster in my mouth.
It smells like a dead, rotten bear.
It looks like the Grim Reaper.
It sounds like a lion roaring.
It feels like a person slapping me.
 . . . Fear.

Cameron Brackley (9)
Edward Worlledge Middle School, Great Yarmouth

Love

Love is pink like candyfloss.
It tastes like white chocolate.
It smells of a warm summer's day.
It looks like a red balloon.
It sounds like birds singing.
It feels like a cosy dressing gown.
 . . . Love.

Sashka Borgenvik (8)
Edward Worlledge Middle School, Great Yarmouth

Fear

Fear is black like a dustbin.
It tastes like a rotten apple.
It smells like a burning fire.
it looks like a howling moon.
It sounds like a dog crying for mercy.
It feels like a rustle of wind.
 . . . Fear.

Lewis Howard (9)
Edward Worlledge Middle School, Great Yarmouth

Jealousy

Jealousy is green like mouldy apples.
It tastes like sour lemons.
it smells like bitter food.
It looks like a damp, misty road.
It sounds like a screaming whale.
It feels like a wet coat.
 . . . Jealousy.

Courtney Emblem (9)
Edward Worlledge Middle School, Great Yarmouth

Scared

It tastes like a horrible gloomy house.
It smells like some rotten flesh.
It looks like a 1,000 year old haunted house.
It sounds like a big family of bats.
It feels like a heart beating fast.
 . . . Scared.

Ben Dowell (9)
Edward Worlledge Middle School, Great Yarmouth

Love

Love is red like a pretty rose.
It tastes like strawberries and cream.
It smells like a fresh day.
It looks like a petal off a rose.
It sounds like rustling trees.
It feels like a bed of flowers.
   . . . Love.

Sophie Brown (8)
Edward Worlledge Middle School, Great Yarmouth

Love

Love is red like a shiny red rose.
It tastes like jam on toast.
It smells like a yummy biscuit.
It looks like a bunch of flowers.
It sounds like birds singing a pretty song.
It feels like puppies being born.
 . . . Love.

Sophie Speight (9)
Edward Worlledge Middle School, Great Yarmouth

Bullies

Every day I awake and think about you bullies
Who've wrecked my life,
Turned it around
Now I dare not make a sound,
As tears start rolling down my eyes,
Because of you - making up lies
About my face, about my hair
Why don't you start taking more care?
Because you're not perfect,
Neither am I,
So why go round, making people cry?

Courtney Farrow (11)
Edward Worlledge Middle School, Great Yarmouth

Feeling Different Feelings

Happy
Happiness feels good
And sometimes feels bad
Probably makes you hyper
Possibly giving you a headache
Yeah, everyone gets happy!

Sad
Sad doesn't feel good,
Annoyed you can feel
Don't put other people down!

Love
Love is like a red, red rose,
Wilting by the hour,
It makes no sense to fall in love
With someone like a flower
'Cause at the end of the day,
You'll be left heartbroken!

Annoyed
Annoyance happens to everyone,
Even Mum and Dad,
Annoyance feels bad,
Everyone gets annoyed!

Kirsty Goodwin (11)
Edward Worlledge Middle School, Great Yarmouth

Time

I want to travel back in time
To see history in action
Perhaps I'll see Monmouth and Lyme
And see his reaction!

I close my eyes and think of war
Hitler's assault on our nation
Where will I travel? I'm not sure
Will I see his reaction?

That war was nasty I want to leave
I'll close my eyes and think of Rome
Through a crowd at the Colosseum I heave
Until I'm ready to head home

The pyramids are next to visit
Before I go I ought to mention
The King's treasure where he hid it
What will be the Pharaoh's reaction?

On the way back at Wembley I'll stop
The '66 World Cup final to catch
On to the hallowed turf I'll hop
I may even score in the match.

Nathan Kurien (9)
Gidea Park College, Romford

Time Twister

Time is so slow
I'm travelling to another dimension
I really wanna go
Can you feel all tension?

Time is speeding up
Just as it was getting good
Oh I'm out of luck
Would stay if I could

Now I'm warping time
Up, down, all around
I think this is a crime
There's no sound

Oh I'm in the dinosaurs' reign
Phew they really stink
Am I just plain insane?
What do you think?

I'm back in my bed now
I think I've been asleep
And I really don't know how
That was *magnifique!*

Briana Longe (10)
Gidea Park College, Romford

Tick-Tock

All the time they twist,
They will never realise,
If they have hit the mist,
Or the object otherwise.

Have they checked the time?
Before they ever stop,
It's nearly half-past nine,
Just check the clock.

They hoped it would stop,
They opened the door,
Just even with a knock,
They could see no more.

They were in a black hole,
They saw a time void,
Just like a mole,
They were annoyed.

They were having a dream,
Time was always ticking,
What a strange theme,
It was like time is thinking.

Samuel Chapman (10)
Gidea Park College, Romford

What If?

What if the clock stops ticking,
Though not for eternity?
What if the hands stop pricking,
The numbers which we see?

What if the pendulum stops swinging
And brings us back in time?
What if the chime stops singing?
I'm sure that it's a crime.

What if a paradox is waiting?
I see myself in the past,
What if it's already creating?
Although it may not last.

What if I go to the future,
Forward a millennium or two?
What if they're all like a torture,
If they have too much that's new?

What if a vortex comes
And sucks you off the ground?
What if it feels like you're doing sums,
Spinning you round and round and round?

Jessica Hawkes (10)
Gidea Park College, Romford

Time Travel

I fly in space to a different era
I find myself in a void
Now I think a bit clearer
But this was something I tried to avoid

I think I am flying in the past
I know I am flying in space
Now I know what is going on at last
I am travelling at a slow pace

I think this voyage is a nightmare
Now I have arrived
I hope people give me love and care
Thank goodness I'm alive

Now I am alone in history
I am in the era of poor old Mary
I hope it is not going to be gory
I think this woman is quite scary

Now that morning is night
Everybody is sleeping
I wish I could still fly
But I can feel real time resuming.

Saif Imran (10)
Gidea Park College, Romford

Time Travel

We are falling through a void
Spinning, turning, don't know what to do
I'm getting quite annoyed
Maybe we might visit 1972.

Through a time shaft we go
Back through time to the dinosaurs' reign
So we go, I have to say, 'No!'
When we go, I hope I don't go insane.

We are there in the prehistoric age
It is getting quite confusing
I don't want any dinosaurs in a rage
Some of us think it is quite amusing.

Back through space and time
Through to the Romans' reign
I hope it is not a crime
I hope I don't get in trouble again.

Back in my bed now
The light is still beaming
Now I'm asleep I don't know how
I still must be dreaming.

Jack Keys (10)
Gidea Park College, Romford

A Twist In Time

The grandfather clock moves from hour to hour,
Time flies so quickly where does it go?
How does it have such strange power?
This is what I will never know.

Time is a wonderful thing,
Sleeping in a nightmare or even a dream,
Travel into time, you would be the king,
Shining everywhere, was that a gleam?

What do I do? I don't know what,
Whirling, spinning, twirling and floating,
I am starting to like this quite a lot,
I am starting to take this all in, gloating.

I can't open my eyes they feel like they've stuck,
I can't move my body, what's going on?
I want to come out of here if I have any luck,
Nobody is here they have all gone.

I am back in my own bed,
Where have I been?
'That was fun,' I said,
Why had nobody seen?

Ankita Gupta (10)
Gidea Park College, Romford

The Reappearing Earth

I fly through time in the air
In the future and in the past
There's a merry-go-round over there
Spinning extremely fast.

The planets all around me
Twirling in the sky
In the space there's gravity
But I have to say goodbye.

The Universe is running
With stars in my eyes
Because it is so cunning
It nearly always dies.

The sleepless nights up here
Always make me moan
I have such a fear
Of all the things that roam.

I love time
It's the best
I always think of a rhyme
To cheer up all the rest.

Rachael Rawlins (9)
Gidea Park College, Romford

Quick Time

While I hear the clocks tick,
I sense lots of danger,
I have been really sick
And now I am lying in a manger.

The planets are churning,
My tummy really hurts,
All around, floating and turning,
Round the corner someone lurks.

Time is passing too quick,
This is a puzzle,
Is this a sort of trick,
Or are they trying to make me dazzle?

As time goes back,
To where it should be,
I realise that someone was slack,
I have been time travelling, now I see.

I jumped into my bed,
The journey had been very tiring,
Things are still in my head
And nature is getting less admiring.

Niharika Thakur (9)
Gidea Park College, Romford

Where Will I Go?

Where will we be going, future, present or past?
We are travelling through time just like Doctor Who.
I want it to be quick, I hope we're going fast,
Also I want to know where, oh please tell us do.

We might end up in the years of the dinosaurs
Or we could end up in the future with flying cars.
There is a chance ending up somewhere with a minotaur!
I think we will have to pass space and Mars.

We are travelling through a massive space,
A giant empty void,
Through the air my ship will race
And go faster I say, annoyed.

Streaks of light are quickly flashing by,
Travelling faster than the speed of light,
Speeding through the void we fly,
I hope there are no aliens I have to fight!

We slow down and land with a bump,
Cannot wait, this is going to be great.
I open the door and out I jump,
Oh no! I am still in 2008!

Jonathan Willans (10)
Gidea Park College, Romford

The Time Twister

I met a time traveller from an antique land
Who warped me into an old time scale
Spinning and turning magically in his hand
Tossed around the universe like a gale

Familiar faces looked younger to me
As I was drawn like a storm to the 70s
Slowly pulsing and quivering I could see
The youthful past of my ancestries

A time dimension, a quantum leap
Gave me an insight of bygone days
The traveller drifting into the deep
Time transformation, a frightening gaze

Men on the moon and cars shaped like bugs
A new era of music and deep coloured flowers
Psychedelic hyper drive, love, peace and hugs
A whistle-stop tour of trembling towers

Pushing the button of teleportation
We evaporate into a time warp track to the future
Our energies sapped by this historical flirtation
A minute has passed during this time warp lecture.

Priya Bhargava (10)
Gidea Park College, Romford

Time Travelling

We thought when we travelled through time
That we would see something there
When we saw somebody cause a crime
We really had no time to spare

We wanted to travel to the Roman generation
To see if people thought it was fair
When we arrived there was a situation
With somebody attacking their lair

We had to travel through a void
To see the Victorian years
But we had to start to avoid
So we decided to swap gears

When we went to the Tudor stage
Where Mary Tudor began to rule
We saw some people who had a rage
Who said Mary Tudor was cruel

We went far back to the past
To see a dinosaur
We saw one that couldn't run very fast
Till it began to roar.

Finley Miles (10)
Gidea Park College, Romford

Time Travel

I am spinning around in nothingness
Surrounded by an eerie atmosphere
I was in a time machine more or less
When everything changed and filled me with fear

Now I am floating and I feel alone
I drop my head to fall asleep
But I am awoken by a piercing tone
Before my eyes I find what I seek

'My time machine!' I exclaim with glee
As I walk up the steps to see
'Now I can start up the engine and flee!
Oh no, where did I leave my key?'

It's not in my bag or in my pocket
It seems to have gone as if by magic
Wherever can it be? Oh, it's in my locket
So really there was no need to panic

I push the buttons and turn the dials
The engine power starts to climb
The clock reads years instead of miles
As I get ready to travel through time!

Afreen Hossain (10)
Gidea Park College, Romford

Time Travel

Have you ever wanted to go into the past?
Ever wanted to fly through space?
Wanted to make happy times last?
A bit like a time race?

Time travel is so misleading,
I felt scared, I felt dizzy,
Going so fast, just like speeding,
My arms and legs felt so fizzy.

Everything had vanished,
I thought I heard a scream,
Like I had been banished,
Wished it was a dream.

Racing through the darkness,
Speeding past the stars,
Heading towards a brightness,
I'd love to travel to Mars.

Travelling to the future,
Travelling to the past,
I will have had a fantastic adventure,
But my machine must travel fast.

Sophie Perry (10)
Gidea Park College, Romford

Pendulous Darkness

Clocks are ticking,
The pendulum is kicking,
The sides of the case,
Like a mace.

The hands are moving,
It's as though they're grooving,
I watch the dial,
Never do I smile.

Then a mist fills the room,
Then I hear a very loud boom!
Then I see numbers passing,
This is even worse than fasting.

Then the room is filled by ticking,
It's as though the pendulum is kicking,
Back and forth, back and forth,
After this I'm going north.

Then a darkness fills the place,
It's as though I'm in space,
Travelling through the dark void,
I even thought my name was Lloyd.

Jonathan Singh (9)
Gidea Park College, Romford

What A Weird World

Suddenly I felt really strange,
I felt as if I was whirling,
This is something I didn't arrange,
Then I felt as if I was twirling.

Stay in the present,
And go back to the past
This is very unpleasant
Because I'm going so fast.

Going into a different dimension,
I think I'm in space,
What an unusual invention,
Or maybe it's just a weird place.

The future lies ahead,
Who knows what it will hold,
Which path we will tread,
On our way to getting old.

Oh no, look at the clock,
I have really got to go,
It has come to me as quite a shock,
But I'll miss you all you know.

Emily Pettitt (10)
Gidea Park College, Romford

What Is Happening?

I can't feel anything,
I can't see or smell,
What is happening?
I can only hear bells.

Would you feel dizzy
Or would you be doubtful?
Would you feel fuzzy
Or would you be frightful?

I can't see the number, it is fuzzy,
I can feel doubtful numbers,
I can't see numbers, I feel dizzy,
My head wants to slumber.

Why am I feeling like this?
Is it because I'm in a time warp?
Why do I feel amiss?
All I can hear is a lot of talk.

Goodbye time I like you,
Though you confused me,
I know you will miss me too,
I am going for a cup of tea!

Chloe Stephenson (9)
Gidea Park College, Romford

A Wrinkle In Time

A wrinkle in time
A blast of mind
The past is full of crime
So look behind

The Vikings shout
The dragons fight
The people run about
This all happens in the night

If I go to 1962
The birds will fly
I hope I don't see you
They fly by

I wish I could stay
But I must go
I will come and play
You will be running from a foe

Back to the portal
Off I go as a whole
I saw an immortal
I go but save my soul.

Fiyinfoluwa Olayide (10)
Gidea Park College, Romford

Different Times

Darkness, *tick-tock*, alone, *tick-tock*,
Nothing around you now silence exists,
Quiet is the underground but the *tick-tock* of the clock,
The weather is cold and I am blinded by the mists.

Swirling through a mysterious time bubble,
Who knows what time it will be or where I will end up?
Seeing patterns as I turn will I end up as a double?
Will I ever get to see my cute little pup?

Whether half-past three or quarter-past nine,
Time will tell you if it's breakfast, lunch or dinner time,
I don't mind digital or analogue whichever way is fine,
But best of all a grandfather clock goes *chime chime chime*.

Time does not stand still for anyone,
A clock's hands go by in its own steady pace,
Most clocks look serious and no clock has fun
Apart from Big Ben backwards and forwards it could be a time race!

A time to read, a time to lead,
A time to rest, a time to nest,
A time to feed, a time to have greed,
But when it's God's time, it's the best.

Tuhina Amin (9)
Gidea Park College, Romford

What Is Red?

Red is a car that is shiny bright,
With its headlight blazing into the night.
Red is a feeling of good inside,
Where there is no place to hide.
Red is a colour of a red red nose,
Red is a colour of a red red rose.
Red is the colour I really like,
Red is the colour that most people like.
Red lighting from the bonfire,
Red is the colour of my brother's car tyre.
Red is a feeling when you are angry,
Red is the grumbling of your tummy when you are hungry.

Caroline Enaw (8)
Goodrington School Ltd, Hornchurch

What Is Red?

Red is a fire, warm and blazing.
Red is a liar, it never tells the truth.
Red is a cooker when it's turned on.
Red is a red car that's never ever gone.
Red is the coolest colour, at least I think it is.
Red is cool, cooler than pink!
Red is my blanket, soft and big.
Red is my shovel for when I dig.
Red is the sun, hot and bright.
Red is great, a beautiful sight.
Red is the rug on my bedroom floor.
Red is the handle, the handle of my door.
Red is the top of the lemonade.
Red bubbles go pop in the cherryade.
Red is ice cream, strawberry of course!
Red makes me scream, happy screams of course.
Red is a pencil long and thin,
Red is a stencil with hearts and flowers.
This keeps me working for hours.

Katherine Leggat (8)
Goodrington School Ltd, Hornchurch

Bullying

Bullies are horrible,
They hurt you a lot,
Don't get them angry
Or they'll give you a shock.

Bullies are stupid and dopey
And stuff,
If they beat you up
Then that's too tough

Terry Blackham (10)
Goodrington School Ltd, Hornchurch

Flowers

Flowers, flowers
May sad showers
Bluebells sing
Church bells ring
Red or white
It can see daylight
Flowers brighten up the day
Lovely colours all through May
Buzzing bees
In the trees
Floating butterflies.

Amy McLean-Nelson (9)
Goodrington School Ltd, Hornchurch

No Way Out

Trapped in a cave
No way out.
In a pit with no walls
No way out.
A girl on a mountain
No way out.
Choosing between either Mum or Dad
No way out.

Is it Mum?

Is it Dad?

Who knows?

She wants to run.
She wants to escape.

But there's no way out.

Caitlin Alice Terry (10)
Goodrington School Ltd, Hornchurch

Bullying

'So what's on TV?' he said gleefully
'Shaun the Sheep,' he replied nervously
There was a dark silence
The boy began to cry
As he went shy

The others called him a baby
And they picked on him
Then they started to kick
He was poked by a stick
As they started to pick
On him!

Jack Harper (10)
Goodrington School Ltd, Hornchurch

Bully

On the street at school
I'm being bullied
Tears falling from my eyes
I can't stop
She hurts me, she hits me
I can't take it any more
What should I do? I don't know
Someone please help me
No one to help, no one to care
I can't be happy in my life of fear.

Funmi Adeotoye (9)
Goodrington School Ltd, Hornchurch

The Bully Round The Corner

I know she's round there
With the big scary hair.
She's round the corner I tell you!
Who? Who's round the corner? Who?
Go and look, she'll be there.
Where? Who is there? Where?
She's not there.
No, nowhere.
OK, I'll be off home then.
But the question is when?
Out of the shadows they came.
That doesn't look like her, is this a game?
No, she thought.
They won't follow if you just walk.
Go away.
Fine, OK.

Acacia London (9)
Goodrington School Ltd, Hornchurch

School

S chool is fun
C oming home is better
H anging out with my friends
O pening presents
O n my birthday
L ooking forward to Friday!

Harrison McCann (9)
Goodrington School Ltd, Hornchurch

Lizards

Lizards are nice,
Some are big,
Some are small,
None are tall.

Lizards eat small vermin,
They won't eat tall people.

Some love water,
Some hate water,
Some love night,
Some hate night,
Some love light,
Some hate light,
They never love people much.

Malagasy lizards change their pattern and colour,
Not only chameleons change their pattern and colour,
Some look like wood,
Some hook like monkeys.

Lizards have wonderful skin colours,
No lizards are forgetful.

They haven't got any fur,
Lizards are fantastic!

Daria Koukoleva (9)
Goodrington School Ltd, Hornchurch

My Cold

I went to school after a very bad flu,
Nothing was the same,
When the register was shouted,
When the name of Fadeke was called it didn't sound the same,
It felt like an echo,
It was a very big pain,
My face was the colour of a horse,
I was so paranoid and scared,
I found myself in the wrong class,
It felt so good to be in my class again.

Jasmine Langan (9)
Goodrington School Ltd, Hornchurch

Day At School

We go to the cloakroom.
The sun shines.
We change our shoes.
Get our work
And go upstairs.
Write our homework in.
Get it checked.
Do our spellings
And get our hymn book.
Go to assembly.
Sing a hymn.
Do the prayer
And go upstairs.

Katie Hastie (9)
Goodrington School Ltd, Hornchurch

Out Of Rugby

8 o'clock comes quickly
Everyone dashes tackles
Their mum's cries are everywhere in the air
Tackle bags are being thrown
I can't take much more
Ed and Ted are fighting.

Xavier Farnham-Pegley (8)
Goodrington School Ltd, Hornchurch

My Dog

My dog is such a wally
He goes straight under my bed if he's scared
His name is Charlie
I don't know why my dog is such a wally

I like him a lot and love him too
He is so weird and I am too
Charlie likes being funny
He is such a wally.

Amy Storrar (9)
Goodrington School Ltd, Hornchurch

The Teacher With The Whistle

I hear a gun in the sky.
I see a boy give a grin.
People see a bee in the tree
And slam it with their feet.
I see a teacher with a whistle
And is very mean.
He put it in his mouth
And blew it with a spin.
The whistle is like the sun.
I'm nearly blind.
People pat their knee because they are hurt.
The teacher is happy and gives a face.

Fadere Sorunke (8)
Goodrington School Ltd, Hornchurch

Hunger

Hunger is black like a black rat, evil and no thought.
It tastes like thoughtlessness and starvation.
It feels like thin air with nothing to spare.
It smells like a workhouse kitchen cooking a toad pie.
It reminds me of disgrace.
It sounds like a calling child shouting for a grain of rice.
It looks like a child being whipped.

Alexandra Le Mesurier (9)
Hainford Primary Partnership, Norwich

I Saw Uranus

I saw Uranus
It was white like a dress
I saw Uranus it was cold like snow.

We saw Uranus
It was shaped like a ball
We saw Uranus
Made of gas most of all.

Step on Uranus
We think you'll die
How fascinating is Uranus
You'll probably want to see.

Katie Grimmer (9)
Hainford Primary Partnership, Norwich

Mars

This planet is ever so red,
As red as something has bled.
It can get very warm and ever so cold.
Craters so vast and big,
It looks like a pretty fresh fig.
This planet is very near,
It gets hit with comets we can almost hear.
It orbits the sun almost still,
The first man on it will be Bill.
It has no aliens at all,
But don't worry, it won't fall!

Grace Mellows (9)
Hainford Primary Partnership, Norwich

Sadness

Sadness is blue like a river of pitiful tears
It sounds like a storm of rain
It smells like mud from an old pond
It tastes like a bowl full of salt
It feels like being in a very dark and cold cellar on your own
It looks like a dream fading away
It reminds me of a very colourful wall that just vanishes.

Sydnie Snowling-Dunford (9)
Hainford Primary Partnership, Norwich

Sadness

Sadness is black like an empty box
It sounds like a crack of thunder
It tastes like out-of-date jelly
It looks like a dead skeleton

It smells like a dead fish
It feels like a massive boulder
It reminds me of when I'm grounded.

Daniel Porter (8)
Hainford Primary Partnership, Norwich

Roses

The sweetest and dearest flower that grows,
Perfect both to see and smell,
Words never, never tell,
Half the beauty of the rose -
Buds open, after a while close,
Petal on petal of the silky rose,
Soft pink or vibrant scarlet.
How amazing to be princess of the rose.

Jessie Rose Ross (10)
Marian Vian Primary School, Beckenham

Victoria

Her name is Victoria,
That's my name too.
She is made of fine porcelain,
Fragile, delicate, with eyes bright blue.
Although a doll, but not a toy,
She certainly brings me lots of joy.
This item I cherish and is a collectable piece,
It is blessed with tranquil peace.
Standing bonny and tall,
Majestically dressed up for any grand ball.
In a fine, jasmine white, laced dress
And looking so bold,
With her long strawberry blonde hair, exceptionally gold.
Pretty as a picture,
She is beautiful enough,
Carrying a pink rose on her left hand cuff.

My special doll takes pride of place
And Victoria is full of lemon grace.

Victoria Addison (11)
St Helen's Primary School, Ipswich

My Special Princess

My special princess is enclosed by a crystal ball
But still she is happy and joyful.
Her dress, crown and ballet shoes are rhubarb-pink.
Her name is Sugar - she has pale pink skin.
There are multicoloured snowflakes
Cascading down her buttermilk hair.
Mum bought me Sugar for Christmas Day
She means a lot to me, my mum.
She bought Sugar because her toffee-cream hair
Reminded her of my goldy hair;
She also bought Sugar because she knows I love pink.
Whenever I look into Sugar's black magic eyes
They make me feel warm and comforted -
Whenever I feel cold and disinherited.

Francesca Mulvey (10)
St Helen's Primary School, Ipswich

Bilko

His paws are prepared to pounce
like pistons on a steam engine,
his legs, once cocoa-brown,
are now partially splattered with dirt.

Bilko's ears seem to come from another woofer
because they are so soft.

Woofer is what my mum used to call him
when he barked at the postman;
he's more obedient now,
although he still whines at him.

He also purrs when he sees someone he knows
like my pale bamboo grandad.

In the park he is never confident;
timidness is his motto!
He is even scared of Jack Russells,
he circles them like a pack of hyenas
and then stays close to me.

His paws prepared to proceed,
he's just like Sergeant Bilko,
they are both cowards.

Oscar Anderson (11)
St Helen's Primary School, Ipswich

Love Can Cushion You

I only found out a year ago
My cousin Olly was moving away
He was going to York, such a far far away place
He tried to get into Cambridge
But my other cousin Max got in this Christmas instead of Olly
So last Christmas they gave this to me
The cushion
I remember my cousins and love them as much as I love my water
baby pink and amethyst purple musical glitter babes cushion
When I listen to my loud music . . .
I imagine my cousin hugging and kissing me
When I am sad and melancholy . . .
I make it a soft sound
When I am happy . . .
I make it deafening sound, as loud as a baby's cry
I think it is magical the way it finds music
Like the way we find friends
A fairytale, as light as my cushion
Fantasy is love and passion.

Elana Muncey (11)
St Helen's Primary School, Ipswich

On My Holiday

On my holidays we went by plane
We didn't go by a taxi
On my holiday we ate chips with burgers
We didn't eat fish
On my holiday I played with my auntie's cat
We didn't play with balloons
On my holiday we saw dolphins
We didn't see a snake
On my holiday we went to the circus
We didn't go swimming
On my holiday I got to go on the computer
We didn't go to the library.

Flora Calivangue (7)
St Helen's Primary School, Ipswich

Flowers

If I were a rose my petals would be as red as the sunset.
If I were a bluebell my bells would ring sweetly.
If I were a dandelion my yellow middle would shine like the sun.
If I were a lily I would open my bright pink petals.
If I were a tulip I would be many colours like a rainbow.
If I were a snowdrop my white drops would be as soft and white
as snow.

Esther Noble (8)
St Helen's Primary School, Ipswich

Underdog

His name was Shoeshine,
He was clumsy all the time.
He never wanted to be,
He just wanted a family.

One day he was taken by the bad guys,
Who were in a devious disguise.
They wanted his DNA,
But Shoeshine got away.

Before Shoeshine got loose,
He got covered in some kind of juice.
But it wasn't juice at all,
It was a special kind of chemical.

The chemical made him pong,
But it also made him strong.
He could speak to you and I,
It also made him fly.

He could hear from miles around,
He could hear the tiniest sound.
He became a super dog,
He became the underdog.

He fought crime everywhere,
He even made a guy lose his hair.
He found a bomb and buried it deep,
Under the earth and left a big heap.

He was a hero,
Everyone's hero,
He was the dog,
The great underdog.

Kean Fry (9)
St Helen's Primary School, Ipswich

When I Was In Spain

There was no rain when I was in Spain
There was sun.
There was no orange squash when I was in Spain
There was blackcurrant squash.
We didn't speak English when I was in Spain,
We spoke Spanish.
We didn't walk on grass when I was in Spain,
We walked on sand.
The pool water wasn't cold when I was in Spain,
It was hot.
We didn't wear clothes when I was in Spain,
We wore swimming costumes.
We didn't sleep in a caravan when I was in Spain,
We slept in a hotel.

Rhiannon Lugo (8)
St Helen's Primary School, Ipswich

Holland

We didn't wear clothes when I was in Holland
We wore swimming trunks!
There were no buses when I was in Holland
There were trams!
They wore clogs when I was in Holland
We wear leather shoes.

Max Bird (7)
St Helen's Primary School, Ipswich

When I Was In Cornwall

I went to Cornwall by car on holiday,
Not train.
It was lovely and hot on holiday,
It wasn't cold.
Loads of men were surfing on holiday,
In Ipswich no one surfs.
We didn't eat pasta in the pub on holiday,
We had fish and chips.
We didn't sunbathe on the beach on holiday,
We body boarded on the waves.
The sea wasn't grey on holiday,
It was sparkly blue.
I didn't go to school on holiday,
I went to big and exciting parks.

Rebecca Rouse (8)
St Helen's Primary School, Ipswich

When I Was At The Beach

It wasn't cold when I was at the beach
I was hot
We didn't wear shoes when I was at the beach
We wore sandals
We didn't eat burgers when I was at the beach
We ate ice cream
We didn't see birds when I was at the beach
We saw seagulls
There weren't flowers when I was at the beach
There was sand
We didn't have small boats when I was at the beach
We had posh boats.

Musomie Aktar (7)
St Helen's Primary School, Ipswich

My Hero

A kind heart
white and silver glasses with gold outlines
as colossal as an aurora

He taught me to bake
a shepherd's pie
the cheese was limited
to avoid overpowering flavours

Inventing a golf club
that keeps your shots straight
he would have liked that

Inventing letters that wrote themselves
greetings cards to see how people were doing
and hope to see you soon cards
just to keep in touch
like a hummingbird interlocked with a microphone
he would have liked that

He would have liked to have seen me all grown up
he should have seen that . . .

His favourite country would probably have been Turkey
he used to cook it in brandy
to make it crisp and rigid.

Stefan Osman-Wiggan (11)
St Helen's Primary School, Ipswich

If You Dare

If you look you'll always see me
If you look I'm always there
If you see me I'll always stare
If you look I'm always waiting . . .

Waiting for you to get out of there

If you know me nothing would be wise
If you know me inside
You'll be waiting to get out
Do you know Heaven and Hell together . . .

That's what I am

I am your nightmares and your dreams
I am your kings and your queens

But I'm not your feelings stuffed inside . . .

Ella Rayment (9)
St Helen's Primary School, Ipswich

I Wish . . .

I wish I could fly like a bird.
I wish I could run like a cheetah.
I wish I could swim like a fish.
I wish I could bloom like a flower.

Molly Gooding (7)
St Helen's Primary School, Ipswich

The Day I Had A Dream

One day . . . I was in my bed I had a dream . . .
In my dream . . . I went to the sun,
I went to the moon,
I went to the butterfly in the cocoon.

The next night I walked through the magic garden . . .
I saw . . . the pixies
I saw the fairies
But the best thing I saw was the magic garden queen

She wore . . .
A bright pink pixie dress
She had wonderful hair
And her wand was made of cress . . .

Then when I woke up I realised that . . .
I was still in my bed
Still with two pillows rested behind my head
Then I wondered what was I doing in the magic garden?
I went to my mum, she said 'How was the magic garden?'
I was wondering how did my mum know what was in my dream?
Was she the magic fairy queen?

Toni-Ann Martin (9)
St Helen's Primary School, Ipswich

Guitarist

Cutting edge sound
The amp is doubling
Noise
Powerful
Strumming
If my strumming was a cartoon
The sound would be in particles

I can't even be bothered
To put on my shoes to play

Jet stream - moonlight
Bay-blue socks
Tap-tap
Up and down on a pedal
Like a soluble weight
On Victorian scales
The shiny black bass
Strikes my rocking eyes

My dad is always telling me
When I get home
To practise so I can learn a new chord
And be like Led Zeppelin
My favourite chords are:
E, C, D, G. (They sound the best).

My influence is my dad
And my grandpa because when I go round there
They are always laughing and playing guitar.

Kingsley Corrall (11)
St Helen's Primary School, Ipswich

My Special Pen

My pen reminds me of
My dad just a bit like a car
He is a monkey, he loves football
He jumps up and down on the bed.
He plays with my guns . . . toy guns
Happy Dad
Never lets me down
When he promises.

Josemar João (11)
St Helen's Primary School, Ipswich

Ruby

Her ebony googly eyes
stare at me every night
like a bursting lavender firework.
The smile twitches at me
even though it's odd.
Every night she jumps into my bed
like a tiger cub getting ready for bed.
Lime green spots with an outline of coastal cream
is her spongy-textured body.
The loose thread comes undone
however many times we stitch it up.
Three fingers wave at me every crescent moon.
Leap,
Hop,
Jump,
My remarkable Ruby.

Alice Todd (10)
St Helen's Primary School, Ipswich

The Necklace

I remember when
I received it all gold and shiny.

It's lava spilt from a volcano
on an island full of yellow joy.

It's got a cross: a cross of happiness.

The pattern reminds me of my family
because my dad is a tetrahedron and I am square.

The sound of this 'noisy pendulum' reminds me
of Barbados and the hot steamy rain.

I recall flying over Bridgetown thinking it was all new,
like a book which turns pages by itself.

I remember the wedding - nearly everyone was there
but my grandad and uncle weren't there . . .

I wish they were.
I imagine that my grandad was wearing this gold and silver necklace.

D'andre Satchwith-Clarke (11)
St Helen's Primary School, Ipswich

Canary

I took the train to London in the holidays,
Joyful place to be,
Glimpse of a lifetime,
A world of records,
The London Eye glaring at the image of me,
An ant in a network
Of a special place.
Meanwhile,
Being glued to Big Ben striking special,
The wondrous Savoy,
What a history!
To be in a bird cage
Of the Canary Warf.
The County Hall
And Nanco Station.
The highest jumper in England
Is
Me!
Triumphant!
As I jump on the colossal bungee jump.
Better than Wroxham,
Hiking in Scandinavia,
Cartwheeling in New York,
Topping them off,
Is London,
In England!

Andrew Bolt (10)
St Helen's Primary School, Ipswich

Doorway!

The door used to be there.
I don't know where it has gone.
Now is only well, a hole, well at least I don't know.
Yesterday I sat there looking in, I can see through to the other side.
I dare not go through it.
I might have to hide.
I believe there are monsters and a magical, dangerous land.
I will try,
I will, I am going to put my foot down.
Wow result,
Nice land with animals and grass and flowers.
I was never scared, it was you all along.
Yes you all along.

Amoke Bowman-Boyles (9)
St Helen's Primary School, Ipswich

Memory Playing With Cats

Memory playing with cats,
Inventing toys out of anything,
Like milk bottle strips,
Kittens kicking them around.

Brushing them about.
Oh - the happiness!
They take them away for the kill,
Toppling from the stairs.
Letting cats destroy them,
Enveloping them in ghost-white fur.

Stampeding them apart,
Tearing them apart,
Ripping them apart.
I see such happiness,
Please let this continue,
Strip-rippers.

Jake Teague (11)
St Helen's Primary School, Ipswich

My Baby Sister

My baby sister was born on the 5th August.
She was as noisy as fire,
She kept on crying,
Although she was cute.
When she came home
She flopped over my lap,
She gave me a big smile,
As proud as a rose,
Growing in a queen's garden.

One month later she was unbelievably naughty
Although I did not know what to do.
Whenever I gaze at her
She sometimes looks like my dad.
Also, when I'm forlorn
She just makes me laugh by staring at me.
Her hair is like a piece of liquorice -
It curls all over the place,
Like scattered snow.
She is a hairdryer
Because of the way she cries.
She was born in Ipswich.
Her eyes are black as black magic.
She was wearing a flowery top in one photograph.
I choose her because she is really special to me
And I love her like sand loves the sea.

Shahnaz Rahman (11)
St Helen's Primary School, Ipswich

The Greatest Cat Ever

I remember him,
When I was young,
He used to bite and scratch,
The pain when he pierced
And when he mauled,
Didn't hurt at all,
Because I loved him
And I always will.

He had bright green eyes,
With organic, swollen ears,
Black and magnolia,
Like a midnight sky in Hawaii,
The time where love
Is where sadness is,
Christmas.

He ran away
When he followed me to school,
The day from then
I never saw him again,
Except for in my heart.

He used to steal my Tigger toy,
Which I thought was hilarious,
I always think about him,
Cascading, white snowflakes,
Jumping on him,
While he chased his tail,
I hope I see him again.

There are still scratch marks on the wall,
For Dustpan,
The best cat I ever had.
I will always remember him.

Tansie Shoults (10)
St Helen's Primary School, Ipswich

Bradley

Bradley. A sweet name, like vanilla ice cream
Covered in chopped strawberries.
He cries at night so we hold him tight.
Sometimes a sweetheart, others a pain.
His eyes are two, first dawn blue,
But when mad, two ferocious fireballs.
They party with each other or fight like eagles.
His laugh is as pleasing as a robin,
But his scream will rip our heart in two.
But this Bradley I love -
Always smiling, always quiet - as still as a Henry Moore statue.
A picture.
Shhh!

Charlie Fitch (11)
St Helen's Primary School, Ipswich

Photograph

I only found out a week ago
But I was broken like a clay sculpture.
My cheerful nature floated away like a stream.
I was devastated,
Tear after tear was streaming down my cool chin.
I loved her like my own sister.
My dad said, 'I am sorry.'
I was too torn to speak.
I felt like shutting down, like a computer,
But most of all . . . I was shocked;
I now hold that picture to my Mediterranean blue heart.
I still don't know how to tell my friends, I just don't.

Charlie Andrews (11)
St Helen's Primary School, Ipswich

When I Was Young

There were no earrings when I was young,
No earrings.
We didn't have skateboards when I was young,
We had buggies.
We didn't have beds when I was young,
We had cots.
When I was young I didn't cry . . . *I screamed!*
I really did!
I didn't have Coke when I was young,
I had milk.
I didn't write when I was young,
I played.
My sister was older than me when I was young,
I was a baby.
I didn't watch 'Tracy Beaker' when I was young,
I watched baby programs.
When I was young I didn't walk,
I crawled.
When I was young I didn't go to the toilet,
I had a potty.
When I was young I didn't have McDonald's,
I had baby food,
But all that was a long time ago . . .

Natasha Smith (7)
St Helen's Primary School, Ipswich

Applaud Me!

Ten dancing daffodils ago,
when his glowing olive face
ran across the jocund park
and shouted
Grass!
The ducks congratulated him
with a great comforting
Quack!

Eight soapy bubbles ago,
when his beaming
blossom countenance
turned a mellow vanilla
as my dad exclaimed
Bathtime!
He used his well-known secret weapon
and manipulated his sweetness,
like Puss in Boots,
eyeing up a scaly sardine,
causing me to whisper
Aww!

Four sticky delicious buns ago,
when his miniature fingers
transformed into chocolate,
after a single, oozing biscuit
Messy!
Inventing a never melting confectionary bar,
which he wasn't allowed,
he did a crazy mango melody
dance to 'Mr Lonely'
thinking . . .
Applaud me!

Tiffany Evripidou (11)
St Helen's Primary School, Ipswich

My Teddy Bear

My bear is called Grace
She is very kind, loving and happy
Also very furry
She is the colour of a water baby
She wears clothes like you and me!
She encourages me
To look forward to after school
Because she will be waiting for me at home
She's just like a pal
That gives me hugs
She has eyes the shape of worn pebbles
From a Cornish beach
Her eyebrows are like a wave
Travelling to the sea.

Joy is when the sun hits your skin
Comfort is her speaking in my ear.

Once she got a sling, when I got hurt
And broke my arm
We matched each other!

Chloe Stygall (10)
St Helen's Primary School, Ipswich

Losing Bessy

I used to enjoy watching Bessy
Staring into the open world
Barking at cars going past
But one day when I was walking to school
There was no dog staring into the cold
No dog barking at cars
Just a damp spot
Then I realised Bessy was gone.

Anna Mulvey (8)
St Helen's Primary School, Ipswich

When I Was In Gran Canaria

It wasn't cold in Gran Canaria,
It was hot.
The sand wasn't cold in Gran Canaria,
It was hot.
The sea wasn't dirty in Gran Canaria,
It was clean.
We didn't eat chicken in Gran Canaria,
We ate fry-ups.
It wasn't boring in Gran Canaria,
It was fun.

Amy Goodger (8)
St Helen's Primary School, Ipswich

Things That Go Chomp In The Night

They lurk in the alleyways
They howl at the moon
Be careful when the sun sets
They'll be out to play soon

Chewing at the skin
Chomping at the eyes
You will feel no pain
But definitely surprise

Feel sorry for the human
That wanders down the street
For in the darkest night-time
They eat anyone they meet

The sun shall protect you
From that deadly foul beast
For it sleeps from 6 till 6
You shall not become its feast.

Emily Grace Wintle (11)
St Michael's Woolmer Green Primary School, Knebworth

A Spooky Sleepover

One spooky, grisly night,
My friends were in store for a fright.
'Let's tell spooky poems,' one of them said.
So this is the poem of the fright of your life . . .

It was a cold, dark night at the graveyards,
Where only someone stood,
Shaking with fear
And her heart pounding as quick as lightning.

Suddenly a mysterious growl!

She ran as fast as she could!
But she was too late . . .
She tripped and the monster was right behind her.

'Argh!' . . .

Mollie McCormack (9)
St Michael's Woolmer Green Primary School, Knebworth

Dreams

A world ahead, things to do,
Wonderful chances to take,
There are great places to visit
And there are places to see too.

If I had a chance to do my dreams
I would take it with no questions,
If you really wanted to achieve your dreams
You can't give up.

There are all different dreams to take,
Being famous or doing things you love,
No one can stop you from
Achieving your dreams.

Daniel Hill (10)
St Michael's Woolmer Green Primary School, Knebworth

The Forbidden Forest

Darkness all around,
The night pitch-black,
Looking around,
Trying to find my way back.

The moon lighting my pathway,
Trees all looking the same,
Darts hitting my back
As it began to rain.

Trying to find my way home,
Looking all around,
I knew I wasn't alone.

There in the darkness,
There in the black,
Someone was waiting
 For the time to attack.

Chloé Allanson (10)
St Michael's Woolmer Green Primary School, Knebworth

Animals

When I went to the zoo
I saw lots of animals,
Big ones like elephants
And little ones like penguins.

I saw a terrifying tiger
With long sharp teeth,
Beautiful stripes,
Bright black and orange.

In the aquarium
I saw a bright blue whale,
Drifting through the water
Like an aeroplane drifting through the air.

And finally I saw
A slithery snake,
Sliding around
With its orange slimy skin.

Daniel Porter (10)
St Michael's Woolmer Green Primary School, Knebworth

Subjects

This is what I told my dad,
Some are good, some are bad.
Some make my brain go bad.

Lunchtime is the best,
Lots of yummy food to eat,
English is great.

Maths is not so great,
So try new subjects,
You never know.

Art is fantastic,
The Tudors are great,
So let's get writing,
This is super,
This is great.

Megan Bone (9)
St Michael's Woolmer Green Primary School, Knebworth

My Brother!

My brother is very tall,
He can reach to the top of the sky
And come back down again.

There is never a lonely time with my brother,
He can always keep me going.

But there is one thing
That nobody else can achieve,
Which is the love and care he gives to me.

So that is why I call him the best,
My love for him
Can't be said in words!

That's why he's *my* brother!

Savannah Lamars (9)
St Michael's Woolmer Green Primary School, Knebworth

Don't Blink Once

A roar of thunder,
A flash of lightning,
The moonlit sky dark and cold,
Why I was there, I don't know.

I took a step to the door,
I breathed slowly and opened it
And a small slow creak was a greeting,
I shivered nervously as I entered.

I took my first steps
Into the crumbling old building,
Not daring to blink once
And I heard a dark voice.

'Why's a boy here?'
I began to panic,
I wanted to run but I couldn't,
And as I said, don't . . . blink . . . once.

Philip Taylor (11)
St Michael's Woolmer Green Primary School, Knebworth

Fear!

Fear is something lurking under your bed,
Fear is a bomb hanging over your head,
Fear is death, pain and agony,
Fear is a nightmare that just keeps coming back.

You never know if you are on your own,
There is someone in the darkness just waiting to get you,
Fear could be all around.

Fear is the darkness at night,
The creatures of dark stay out till light.
Don't make a noise, don't make a sound,
I have a feeling that fear is around.

You can never be too safe
Because darkness is everything and everywhere.

Matthew Haumann (9)
St Michael's Woolmer Green Primary School, Knebworth

Night!

All alone,
Dark outside,
The midnight sky,
Ice-cold shivers
Coming down my spine.
A hoot, a wolf
Howling at the moon.

Groans and screams
Sounding all around,
A shadow passing
Right through me.
So scared,
So alone,
Nowhere to go!
The graveyard gates open
As I could hear
Voices all around.

Getting ever so close,
The noises making me mad,
The shouts and screams deafening me.

I ran,
It turned me crazy,
Forever running,
So frightened.
The moonlight shimmering down on me.
Running home screaming.

I never stood out at night again!
Because night is when everything changes!

Kieran Mason (11)
St Michael's Woolmer Green Primary School, Knebworth

A Lonely Boy

A lonely boy on the swings,
Feels missed, left out, has to go back into class
When the bell rings.

Has no friends at all,
He feels like a fool.

He wishes he had someone by his side,
Could you take that step? Would you mind?

Every playtime on the swings, no hope for him
And every day going home alone.

He needs a friend he can trust,
Will you be that person? You must!

Lewis Robins (10)
St Michael's Woolmer Green Primary School, Knebworth

My Bunny Is . . .

A mazingly angelic, with a smile on his face,
B eautiful bouncy as he hops around the place,
C ute as a baby, but not that old,
D aring and bold, without being told,
E nergetic and polite,
G raceful and light like a fairy in flight,
H appy just running around on the ground,
I 'm happy that he is who he is.

J umpy and bouncy like a mini kangaroo,
K ind to young animals as he watches them chew,
L ovely and warm to hug on a cold day,
M agical to watch play,
N aughty at times before he goes to sleep.

O bservant and quick to come to his name,
P layful and cute while playing a game,
Q uiet and shy when he is frightened,
R ock star at night, when he needs to enlighten,
S lips into dreamland, while he waits for a new day.

T imid and shy when birds are above,
U ntil passes a small white dove,
V ery small and young and quick to learn new tricks,
W hen I come home he always licks,
EX cellent at jumping high over the trees,
Y awning and swaying in the breeze,
Z igging and zagging on the way to eat food from his bowl.

Lauren Payne (10)
St Paul's CE JMI Primary School, Kings Langley

Rabbits' Fun

Running rabbits darting everywhere
Amazing rabbits with fluffy tails
Bouncing rabbits bouncing here and there
Baby rabbits so cute and soft
Incredible rabbits so cuddly
Tiny rabbits tired and small
Soft baby rabbits so muddy
Fluffy baby rabbits like little fluff balls
Unique rabbits with spots
Nibbling lots and lots!

Libby Radford (10)
St Paul's CE JMI Primary School, Kings Langley

Alphabet Of Disgusting Habits

A is for Alfie who bites his nails.

B is for Ben who is really frail.

C is for Chloe who is really rude.

D is for Dot who runs around nude.

E is for Elle who never says thanks.

F is for Frankie who always burns cakes.

G is for Gail whose hair's always messy.

H is for Hannah who's always fussy.

I is for Ian who always laughs.

J is for Josh who never takes baths.

K is for Kat who wants to be Queen.

L is for Lewis who never wants to be seen.

M is for Molly who's mean to the boys.

N is for Norris who never makes noise.

O is for Olivia who has a pool.

P is for Perry who enjoys school

Q is for Quin who picks his nose.

R is for Ruth who likes to pose.

S is for Steph who plays on the PC.

T is for Tillie who likes TV.

U is for Unith who has smelly feet.

V is for Vicky who likes to cheat.

W is for William who eats lots of lunch.

X is for Xanthe whose friends are a bunch.

Y is for Yvonne who kicks the dog.

Z is for Zack who thinks he's a frog.

Georgia Ware (11)
St Paul's CE JMI Primary School, Kings Langley

Horrible Habits

A is for Andrew who always laughs.
B is for Betty who never takes baths.
C is for Carl who makes too much noise.
D is for Dianne who flirts with the boys.
E is for Eleanor who picks her nose.
F is for Fred who wears too many clothes.
G is for Gill who smashes her phone.
H is for Hannah who won't stop to moan.
I is for Ivy who bites her nails.
J is for Josh who rides on whales.
K is for Kate who stands on tables.
L is for Lucy who is obsessed with labels.
M is for Matt who always falls over.
N is for Nora who collects Rovers.
O is for Oliver who is always bossy.
P is for Penny who turns up mossy.
Q is for Queenie who always lies.
R is for Robert who can't stop eating pies.
S is for Steph who is always rough.
T is for Tom who is always buff.
U is for Una who likes eating bugs.
V is for Vikki who always wears Uggs.
W is for William who talks a lot.
X is for Xerxes who is such a clot.
Y is for Yasmin who never has showers.
Z is for Zoe who can't spell hours.

Joshua White (10)
St Paul's CE JMI Primary School, Kings Langley

Here Come The Cannons

Here come the cannons
They're coming today
Protecting us from the armada
Hip hip hooray
The ones who are evil and
For whom we do not pray
The ones that harm our families
And crave death and pain.

Robert Braban (10)
St Paul's CE JMI Primary School, Kings Langley

My Dog

A dog is hard work, they need love and care
If you don't mind a wet tongue and a lot of hair
A dog is for you

A dog is sweet and is there for you forever
A dog is not just for playing however
A dog is caring

A dog can stay on your sofa and just relax
With you while you just sit back
A dog is loyal

A dog has big brown eyes and a sad face
And she will leave a biscuit trace
A dog is cute

And a dog is not just for Christmas, they're there forever
They will leave you never, never
A dog has feelings

And to sum up this entire poem about dogs is that
Anyone who has a dog will feel differently after you get one
Only three more lines
A dog needs love and a caring house
Not some family who won't give them great times
A dog will be there through everything.

Chloe Coxill (10)
St Paul's CE JMI Primary School, Kings Langley

My Friend Is Amazing!

My friend is amazing
She's good at work
She's mad and never stops smiling
Even if she's down
She's always the victim to tickle at school
She'll always stay the same
Unless she moves to boarding school
Which isn't a surprise!

Molly Gurr (11)
St Paul's CE JMI Primary School, Kings Langley

Animals Galore!

A is for antelope, soft,
B ouncy and energetic,
C is for cheetah, fast,
D aring and strong,
E is for emu, soft,
F luffy and light,
G is for giraffe, tall,
H ungry and long,
I is for iguana, sleepy,
J umpy and hot,
K is for killer whale, hunting,
L azy and big,
M is for monkey, hanging,
N oisy and naughty,
O is for octopus, hiding,
P atient and swimming,
Q is for quail, prancing,
R acing and plump,
S is for snake, slithering,
T idy and sweet,
U is for umbrella bird, flying,
V ery quick and darting here and there,
W is for walrus, lazy,
EX traordinary, fat and hairy,
Y is for yacht, humongous,
Z ipping and zagging.

Emily Hardway (11)
St Paul's CE JMI Primary School, Kings Langley

Animals From The Alphabet

A is for ant as small as a nail
B is for butterfly who sits on snails
C is for cat who pounces his prey
D is for dog who is lively all day
E is for elephant who is slow as a snail
F is for frog who hops on its tail
G is for giraffe who runs with the wind
H is for hermit crab who is never seen
I is for iguana who is as buzzy as a bee
J is for Jamaican fish who is very big
K is for kangaroo who is jumpy like you
L is for lion who lays in the sun
M is for monkey who swings round tree trunks
N is for nano some kind of fish
O is for octopus who swims in the sea
P is for pony who potters around
Q is for quail with huge eyes
R is for rhino charging round and round
S is for snake slithery and round
T is for tortoise over 100 years old
U is for unicorn in your fantasy dreams
V is for vulture that is not what it seems
W is for whale who is gentle and soft
X is for xanepus some kind of frog
Y is for yak
Z is for zebra that is black, white and stripy.

Joely Harris (11)
St Paul's CE JMI Primary School, Kings Langley

The Wonderful World Of My Weird Brother

My brother is something you'd find on a wildlife show
He likes bugs, bees and millipedes
He's incredibly bright and very up tight
And his bark is worse than his bite.

My brother is like a pair of glasses
He's square like a chair and very unfair
He is as mad as a snake and stiff as a rake
And strange in various other ways.

Although I say all these mean things
I've never regretted it once
You see my brother he is the weird type
But without him there would be no fun.

Lillian Holmes (11)
St Paul's CE JMI Primary School, Kings Langley

Spring

S pring is here.
P rimroses gleam in the glistening sunlight.
R oses sway in the strong wind.
I n the sky the sun shone beautifully.
N ew flowers spring from the grassy ground.
G rass sparkled with the dew on it.

Curtis Lake (10)
St Paul's CE JMI Primary School, Kings Langley

Monsters

M onsters give you a fright in the night
O n them they have big long hairs
N o one likes them but I do
S *plash!* There he goes dribbling on my sofa
T hey eat slimy slithery snails, *yuck!*
E xactly on time through your window
R ushing to the dark scary woods
S eriously scary, you won't like them in bed with you.

Harrison Wheeler (8)
St Pierre School, Leigh-on-Sea

The Lion

The big lion
The big, golden lion
The big, golden, fuzzy lion
The big, golden, fuzzy, scary lion
The big, golden, fuzzy, scary, white lion
But when I looked properly
I saw it was my big, golden, fuzzy, scary, white, pet dog!

Lily Ella Bovill (8)
St Pierre School, Leigh-on-Sea

Chelsea FC

C helsea is the best
H ome of Stamford Bridge
E asy to be at the top
L et us win the league
S uper Frank!
E veryone supports Chelsea
A lways winning

F ootball is the best
C ome on Chelsea FC!

Andrew Snell (8)
St Pierre School, Leigh-on-Sea

Bedtime

B edtime is the worst time of the day,
E veryone has a fear when they lay,
D oing nothing in bed laying down feeling dread,
T onight I had an awful dream about my family and I being dead,
I had a dreadful dream last night,
M y bed was scary but I was tucked in tight,
E very night I have a bad dream, especially when I hear a scream!

Ella Kingsbury (8)
St Pierre School, Leigh-on-Sea

Gerty Grime

Once there lived a wicked witch,
Whose name was Gerty Grime.
Every day she cast a spell,
It went wrong all the time.

One day she tried to cast a spell,
But she messed it up.
Now her house has disappeared,
And she lives in an old teacup.

Joshua Bull (7)
St Pierre School, Leigh-on-Sea

Wresting

W WE rules
R ough is a wrestler's middle name
E veryone likes wrestling
S ome wrestlers are champions
T roublemakers are some wrestlers
L osers are some wrestlers
I n the ring people risk their lives
N one goes out of the ring without being hurt
G reat wrestlers are famous.

Rupert Abel (9)
St Pierre School, Leigh-on-Sea

Happiness Is . . .

Happiness is a slow blue lake.
Happiness is a shiny family photo.
Happiness is the breeze of the wind.
Happiness is stickiness of glue.
Happiness is when the pool is cold.
Happiness is our joyful red jumpers.
Happiness is the sight of a TV.

Chloe Quinton (9)
Springfield Junior School, Ipswich

Happiness Is . . .

Happiness is watching my widescreen TV
Happiness is playing on my laptop
Happiness is playing with my dog
Happiness is putting my feet up on the recliner chairs
Happiness is last of all in bed with my cuddly rabbit.

Caitlin Chatfield (9)
Springfield Junior School, Ipswich

Happiness Is . . .

Happiness is when I'm with my dog,
We like playing with the ball.
Happiness is loving my dog.
Happiness is caring for my dog.
Happiness is giving a bone to my dog.
Happiness is looking after my dog.
Happiness is putting him to bed.

Gemma Addison (8)
Springfield Junior School, Ipswich

Happiness Is . . .

Happiness is the sight of TV
Happiness is when Chelsea win
Happiness is when I have got lots of money
Happiness is when I have lots of food
Happiness is playing on my Wii.

Kyle Ferguson (9)
Springfield Junior School, Ipswich

Happiness Is . . .

H appiness is Burger King it
A lways cheers me up
P laying colouring
P laying on my laptop and reading my books
Y oghurt makes me happy and money

Happy!

Kathy Burch (9)
Springfield Junior School, Ipswich

Happiness Is . . .

Happiness is playing with my pets, I have so many
And it's really great 'cause they're all friendly.
Happiness is spending time with my parents,
One's a lady and one's a gent.
Happiness is drawing,
It gets your mind crawling.
Happiness is dancing,
Hopping, skipping, prancing.
Lots of things make you happy,
Happy, happy, happy!

Holly Brown (9)
Springfield Junior School, Ipswich

Happiness Is . . .

Happiness is making things out of Lego
Happiness is listening to music on the computer
Happiness is looking at maps
Happiness is playing on my Wii
Happiness is going to Legoland
Happiness is playing on my iPod.

Calvin Footer (9)
Springfield Junior School, Ipswich

Happiness Is . . .

Happiness is playing with your best friends.
Happiness is shopping with your friends.
Happiness is being with your mum and dad.
Happiness is laughing with your best friends.
Happiness is jumping on the sofa.
Happiness is eating ice cream.
Happiness is planting flowers.
Happiness is playing with your dog.

Téa Addison (8)
Springfield Junior School, Ipswich

Happiness Is . . .

Happiness is going to school and doing art
Happiness is playing ball with my dog
Happiness is when I go to bed and have quiet sisters
Happiness is doing ICT at school
Happiness is when I have pizza
Happiness is when I play with my friends
Happiness is when I eventually fall asleep
Happiness is when my sisters be nice to me
Happiness is when it's night-time
Happiness is when I have a swim
Happiness is when I play with my toys
Happiness is when I have good times
Happiness is when I sit down
Happiness is when I have tea
Happiness is when I go home from school
Happiness is when it's my birthday
Happiness is when I get things
Happiness is when I win something
Happiness is when I go to London
Happiness is when I have a carrot.

Luke Addison (8)
Springfield Junior School, Ipswich

Happiness Is . . .

Happiness is the love of my family
Happiness is the love of my friends
Happiness is the love of my pets
Happiness is the joy of the world
Happiness is playing with my friends
Happiness is playing with my family
Happiness is playing on the Game Cube
Happiness is playing on the PS2.

William Seager (9)
Springfield Junior School, Ipswich

Happiness Is . . .

Happiness is playing on the swing
Happiness is going out rollerskating
Happiness is riding horses
Happiness is eating ice cream
Happiness is making a snowman.

Jessica Harrison (8)
Springfield Junior School, Ipswich

Happiness Is . . .

Happiness is eating fish and chips from the chip shop wrapper.
Happiness is playing CSI on my Xbox 360.
Happiness is when there is a party to go to.
Happiness is when you swing on your chair.
Happiness is playing with my friends.

Ivan Trewern (9)
Springfield Junior School, Ipswich

Happiness Is . . .

Happiness is when the food gets put on the table
Happiness is the chocolate chilling
Happiness is a song that's sung
Happiness is having a family photo
Happiness is when I get pocket money on Saturdays.

Bethany Brown (8)
Springfield Junior School, Ipswich

Happiness Is . . .

Happiness is playing Driver on my Nintendo Wii.
Happiness is playing with dogs.
Happiness is stroking cats.
Happiness is watching Ipswich Town win.
Happiness is when there is no school.

Kai Coe (8)
Springfield Junior School, Ipswich

My Friend Bo

Did you know, that my friend Bo
Is my 'bestest' friend of all?
She runs around and wags her tail
And can even catch a ball!

My friend Bo I have you know
Licks me when she's happy
And when she gets excited -
She can even get quite yappy!

Did you know that my friend Bo
Likes running in the park
And when she tries to talk to me
She often only barks!

My friend Bo you may not know
Is the bestest *dog of all.*

Jessica Lacey (8)
Westwood Primary School, Hadleigh

Sunset

Sunset, sunset so colourful
You're pink and you're purple
Shining like a glittery ball
We can see your reflection nice and sweet
Come down now we're falling asleep
You're floating in the air like a graceful feather
Round and round like a sparkly star
Your shadow is like a disco light
You're bright and sparkly like a shining car
You're so powerful like a bolt of lightning
Sunset, sunset so colourful
Now fall asleep I'll see you soon.

Rosie Pountney (8)
Westwood Primary School, Hadleigh

Young Writers Information

We hope you have enjoyed reading this book - and that you will continue to enjoy it in the coming years.

If you like reading and writing poetry drop us a line, or give us a call, and we'll send you a free information pack.

Alternatively if you would like to order further copies of this book or any of our other titles, then please give us a call or log onto our website at www.youngwriters.co.uk

**Young Writers Information
Remus House
Coltsfoot Drive
Peterborough
PE2 9JX**

(01733) 890066